KU-453-351

English:
Mini-Comprehensions

Inference
Book 1

How to use this book to make the most of 11 plus exam preparation

It is important to remember that for 11 plus exams there is no national syllabus, no pass mark and no retake option. It is therefore vital that your child is fully primed to perform to the best of their ability so that they give themselves the best possible chance on the day.

Unlike similar publications, the **First Past The Post®** series uniquely assesses your child's performance on a question-by-question basis, helping to identify areas for improvement and providing suggestions for further targeted tests. By entering the unique Peer-Compare access code for this book on our website, your child's performance can be compared anonymously to that of others who have taken the same tests.

English: Mini-Comprehensions Inference

This collection of exercises focuses on the roughly 20% of comprehension questions in 11 plus exams that are inference-based. They are useful practice for the standard comprehension section of contemporary multi-discipline 11 plus exams. The six questions accompanying each passage test the student's ability to draw inferences from the text, based on factual information and description.

Never has it been more useful to learn from mistakes!

Students can improve by as much as 15%, not only by focused practice, but also by targeting any weak areas.

How to manage your child's practice

To get the most up-to-date information, visit our website, www.elevenplusexams.co.uk, the UK's largest online resource for 11 plus, with over 65,000 webpages and a forum administered by a select group of experienced moderators.

About the authors

The Eleven Plus Exams' **First Past The Post®** series has been created by a team of experienced tutors and authors from leading British universities.

Published by Technical One Ltd t/a Eleven Plus Exams

With special thanks to the children who tested our material at the Eleven Plus Exams centre in Harrow.

ISBN: 978-1-912364-14-5

Copyright © ElevenPlusExams.co.uk 2017

Second edition

elevenplusexams
head for success

About Us

At Eleven Plus Exams, we supply high-quality, specialist 11 plus tuition for your children. Our website at **www.elevenplusexams.co.uk** is the largest in the UK that specifically prepares children for the 11 plus exams We also provide online services to schools and our *First Past the Post* range of books has been well-received by schools, tuition centres and parents.

Eleven Plus Exams is recognised as a trusted and authoritative source. We have been quoted in numerous national newspapers, including *The Telegraph, The Observer,* the *Daily Mail* and *The Sunday Telegraph,* as well as on national television (BBC1 and Channel 4), and BBC radio.

Our website offers a vast amount of information and advice on the 11 plus, including a moderated online forum, books, downloadable material and online services to enhance your child's chances of success. Set up in 2004, the website grew from an initial 20 webpages to nearly more than 65,000 today, and has been visited by millions of parents. It is moderated by experts in the field, who provide support for parents both before and after the exams.

Don't forget to visit **www.elevenplusexams.co.uk** and see why we are the market's leading one-stop shop for all your 11 plus needs. You will find:

- ✓ Comprehensive quality content and advice written by 11 plus experts

- ✓ Eleven Plus Exams online shop supplying a wide range of practice books, e-papers, software and apps

- ✓ Lots of FREE practice papers to download

- ✓ Professional tuition service

- ✓ Short revision courses

- ✓ Year-long 11 plus courses

- ✓ Mock exams tailored to reflect those of the main examining bodies

978-1-912364-60-2	Verbal Reasoning: Cloze Tests Book 1 - Mixed Format
978-1-912364-61-9	Verbal Reasoning: Cloze Tests Book 2 - Mixed Format
978-1-912364-78-7	Verbal Reasoning: Cloze Tests Book 3 - Mixed Format
978-1-912364-79-4	Verbal Reasoning: Cloze Tests Book 4 - Mixed Format
978-1-912364-62-6	Verbal Reasoning: Vocabulary Book 1 - Multiple Choice
978-1-912364-63-3	Verbal Reasoning: Vocabulary Book 2 - Multiple Choice
978-1-912364-64-0	Verbal Reasoning: Vocabulary Book 3 - Multiple Choice
978-1-912364-65-7	Verbal Reasoning: Vocabulary, Spelling and Grammar Book 1 - Multiple Choice
978-1-912364-66-4	Verbal Reasoning: Vocabulary, Spelling and Grammar Book 2 - Multiple Choice
978-1-912364-68-8	Verbal Reasoning: Vocabulary in Context Level 1
978-1-912364-69-5	Verbal Reasoning: Vocabulary in Context Level 2
978-1-912364-70-1	Verbal Reasoning: Vocabulary in Context Level 3
978-1-912364-71-8	Verbal Reasoning: Vocabulary in Context Level 4
978-1-912364-74-9	Verbal Reasoning: Vocabulary Puzzles Book 1
978-1-912364-75-6	Verbal Reasoning: Vocabulary Puzzles Book 2
978-1-912364-76-3	Verbal Reasoning: Practice Papers Book 1 - Multiple Choice
978-1-912364-77-0	Verbal Reasoning: Practice Papers Book 2 - Multiple Choice

978-1-912364-02-2	English: Comprehensions Classic Literature Book 1 - Multiple Choice
978-1-912364-03-9	English: Comprehensions Classic Literature Book 2 - Multiple Choice
978-1-912364-05-3	English: Comprehensions Contemporary Literature Book 1 - Multiple Choice
978-1-912364-06-0	English: Comprehensions Contemporary Literature Book 2 - Multiple Choice
978-1-912364-08-4	English: Comprehensions Non-Fiction Book 1 - Multiple Choice
978-1-912364-09-1	English: Comprehensions Non-Fiction Book 2 - Multiple Choice
978-1-912364-23-7	English: Comprehensions Poetry Book 1 - Multiple Choice
978-1-912364-14-5	English: Mini Comprehensions - Inference Book 1
978-1-912364-15-2	English: Mini Comprehensions - Inference Book 2
978-1-912364-16-9	English: Mini Comprehensions - Inference Book 3
978-1-912364-11-4	English: Mini Comprehensions - Fact-Finding Book 1
978-1-912364-12-1	English: Mini Comprehensions - Fact-Finding Book 2
978-1-912364-21-3	English: Spelling, Punctuation and Grammar Book 1
978-1-912364-22-0	English: Spelling, Punctuation and Grammar Book 2
978-1-912364-00-8	English: Practice Papers Book 1 - Multiple Choice
978-1-912364-01-5	English: Practice Papers Book 2 - Multiple Choice
978-1-912364-17-6	Creative Writing Examples

978-1-912364-30-5	Numerical Reasoning: Quick-Fire Book 1
978-1-912364-31-2	Numerical Reasoning: Quick-Fire Book 2
978-1-912364-32-9	Numerical Reasoning: Quick-Fire Book 1 - Multiple Choice
978-1-912364-33-6	Numerical Reasoning: Quick-Fire Book 2 - Multiple Choice
978-1-912364-34-3	Numerical Reasoning: Multi-Part Book 1
978-1-912364-35-0	Numerical Reasoning: Multi-Part Book 2
978-1-912364-36-7	Numerical Reasoning: Multi-Part Book 1 - Multiple Choice
978-1-912364-37-4	Numerical Reasoning: Multi-Part Book 2 - Multiple Choice

978-1-912364-43-5	Mathematics: Mental Arithmetic Book 1
978-1-912364-44-2	Mathematics: Mental Arithmetic Book 2
9/8-1-912364-45-9	Mathematics: Worded Problems Book 1
978-1-912364-46-6	Mathematics: Worded Problems Book 2
978-1-912364-52-7	Mathematics: Worded Problems Book 3
978-1-912364-47-3	Mathematics: Dictionary Plus
978-1-912364-50-3	Mathematics: Crossword Puzzles Book 1
978-1-912364-51-0	Mathematics: Crossword Puzzles Book 2
978-1-912364-48-0	Mathematics: Practice Papers Book 1 - Multiple Choice
978-1-912364-49-7	Mathematics: Practice Papers Book 2 - Multiple Choice

978-1-912364-87-9	Non-Verbal Reasoning: 2D Book 1 - Multiple Choice
978-1-912364-88-6	Non-Verbal Reasoning: 2D Book 2 - Multiple Choice
978-1-912364-85-5	Non-Verbal Reasoning: 3D Book 1 - Multiple Choice
978-1-912364-86-2	Non-Verbal Reasoning: 3D Book 2 - Multiple Choice
978-1-912364-83-1	Non-Verbal Reasoning: Practice Papers Book 1 - Multiple Choice

Contents

This workbook has 50 exercises comprising 35 fiction passages and 15 non-fiction passages, each with six questions. The recommended time for each exercise is 5 minutes.

BLANK PAGE

vi

FIRST PAST THE POST®

Mini-Comprehensions

Inference

Fiction

Exercise 1 - A Coastal Walk

Miranda strode out along the clifftop path with her long red hair streaming out behind her in the bracing wind. Wild waves crashed against the rocks below her, buffeting the shore relentlessly with white, salty spray. Although the sun shone down strongly, hazy clouds covered the great yellow disc, diluting its brightness. Budding daffodils were bursting forth from the emerald grass, gorse bushes proudly displayed their bold yellow flowers, and blossom itched to erupt from its imprisoning buds.

Once far enough away from the nearest house, Miranda leant down and unclipped Max's lead from his collar. He lolloped off across the fields joyfully, his long ears flapping behind him and his pink tongue hanging haphazardly out of his mouth. He splashed recklessly through muddy puddles, spraying a nearby family who were enjoying their first ice creams of the season. Miranda sighed as she called out an apology to the muddied walkers. She enjoyed the fact that she no longer needed to rush to get back before it got dark any more, as sunset was not for another couple of hours. For the third year running, Max was refusing to grow up and cease his puppy-like behaviours; he ran full circuit around the field, before bounding off into the next one in pursuit of a rabbit.

1. **Where is Miranda?**

   she is on the clifftop path

2. **At what time of year is this passage set?**

   (illegible handwriting)

3. **What is Max?**

   a dog

4. **Why does Miranda apologise to the walkers?**

   because Max had splashed them in water

5. **What time of day is it?**

   afternoon

6. **How old is Max?**

   3 years old

Exercise 2 - Café Rush Hour

Phillip dashed as quickly as he could back to the kitchen, carefully and politely weaving his way between the packed tables whilst expertly balancing a tower of used coffee cups and plates on his right arm. Midweek was always the busiest time here because local businesses gave everyone the afternoon off, but today was especially busy: all the outside tables were full, as well as those inside, as people enjoyed basking in the warm afternoon sun opposite the town's picturesque park.

Phillip glanced at the clock just as it began to chime four o'clock; he had only been on shift for two hours so far, but it felt like eight! He didn't mind though: he loved serving all his regular customers their favourite afternoon treats and hearing about their day.

Finally, as the clock signalled six o'clock and he ushered the last customers out, he sat down heavily in a large, worn armchair with his own cup of coffee and a book.

1. **What is Phillip's job?**

He is a waitor a t at a cage.

2. **What day of the week is it?**

It is midweek (wednesday)

3. **Why was today 'especially busy'?**

It was busy because on wendresdays every one gets the after noon of in local businesses.

4. **At what time did Phillip's shift start?**

2 o'clock.

5. **Why did Phillip like his job?**

Because he loved serving all the regular customers and hearing about there day.

6. **At what time did the café close?**

6 o'clock

Exercise 3 - Travel Plans

After watching the man searching through the shelves of the travel section for a good ten minutes, Megan thought it was time that she went over to offer some help. She asked where he was planning to go and what kind of travel-guide he was looking for, before he revealed that he was planning to choose a holiday based on a tempting travel book.

"That's a novel way of doing things," she thought. Never had she encountered someone who decided where to go in such a way!

Eventually, he settled on a book about Belize, which recommended several exciting, intrepid expeditions along the three main rivers. Megan pointed out that flights to Central America were expensive and that he would need lots of travel vaccinations, however, he already had most necessary travel jabs after previous adventures in Nepal and Brazil.

1. Where is this passage set?

_____

2. Why did Megan presume that the man was planning to go somewhere?

_____

3. What does the word 'novel' mean?

_____

4. Why had Megan advised many customers before?

_____

5. Where is Belize?

_____

6. Which two continents do we know the man has already visited?

_____

Exercise 4 - The Final Ascent

The rocky ground began to slope even more steeply as the group neared the last one hundred metres of their climb. The expedition was on its final day of a three-day ascent, and was expected to take a similar amount of time to return back to base camp. However, the bitter-cold, biting winds and exhausting climb were all worth it for the amount of money the team had succeeded in raising for Unicef, and their current total was likely to increase once they shared the success of their climb with everyone back home. Everyone in the group had a personal reason to raise money, as Unicef had helped each of them at some point in their lives.

As they finally stood on the summit, they looked back down the slope at the six tracks of footprints snaking away beneath them, and felt an overwhelming sense of pride at their achievement.

1. What are the team climbing?

A mountian hill

2. For approximately how many weeks is the expedition expected to last?

?

3. For what type of organisation is the expedition raising money?

Unicef.

4. Why would the amount of money they had raised soon increase?

It would itch as when they share their success

5. Why had the group chosen to support Unicef?

Unicif had helped each of them once in their lives

6. How many people are in the group?

6

Exercise 5 - A New Restaurant

Andy tossed yet another pizza dough in the air, the tenth of the evening already and it was only 7.30pm! His colleague next to him, Amanda, had been serving up a similar number of pasta dishes since the restaurant had opened an hour and a half ago.

The restaurant was the most popular in town, despite opening only six months ago, but this was expected given the extensive experience of the head chef, who had worked in several top restaurants across Italy. All the local newspapers had written rave reviews on its opening night, praising the novel flavour combinations, charming waiting staff and relaxed atmosphere.

The chefs working there believed it was only a matter of time before they began to receive glowing reviews in national newspapers as well, which would surely bring many more people into the area. Ultimately, the head chef's main motivation for her work was to allow even more people to enjoy good, fresh and delicious food for reasonable prices.

1. What type of cuisine does the restaurant serve?

    _____

2. What time did the restaurant open?

    _____

3. Why is it surprising that the restaurant was so popular?

    _____

4. What is the likely reason for the restaurant's success?

    _____

5. Why would national newspaper reviews be a good thing?

    _____

6. Why did the head chef set up the restaurant?

    _____

Exercise 6 - A Long Plane Journey

People in the terminal watched as the plane rumbled awake and began to pick up speed, hurtling down the runway for take-off. The passengers sighed as they resigned themselves to the cramped seats for the next eleven hours, hoping to get some sleep during the rocking of the flight.

Suddenly, a high-pitched alarm jolted everyone out of their sleep and oxygen masks began dropping down from the ceiling. Panic ensued. The captain hurriedly checked all screens and dials for error messages, and instructed her co-pilot and cabin crew to do the same. The co-pilot shook his head in confusion because he could not find anything that hinted at a problem.

Eventually, after checking every last possibility, the captain called off the alarm and informed the passengers calmly that there was no need to panic and that it had been a false alarm. Several hours later, everyone disembarked, much shaken from the flight's events, but safely delivered to their destination.

1. What is the nearest building to the plane at the start of the passage?

_____

2. Why did the passengers sigh?

_____

3. How long was the flight?

_____

4. Why did the captain check for error messages?

_____

5. Why did the captain tell the passengers that there was no need to panic?

_____

6. Why were the passengers 'much shaken'?

_____

Exercise 7 - A Day Out at Wimbledon

Simon filed along the row and sat down happily with his bowl of strawberries and cream. The two players were just marching out onto court, determinedly carrying their rackets over their shoulders. The ball boys and girls were rolling the bright yellow balls along the sides of the court. All preparations were in full swing and the tension was rising.

Simon always enjoyed his annual trip to Wimbledon: everyone was always in a good mood, the sun was out and there were strawberries and cream on sale everywhere.

Way down below him on the court, the players were warming up, knocking balls back and forth across the net with their usual 'bop' sound. The outcome of this match was important: it was the Women's Singles Final, so whoever won would win the Championship. Simon leaned forward on the edge of his seat as the match began...

1. What sport is about to be played?

_____

2. Why is the tension rising?

_____

3. How often does Simon go to Wimbledon?

_____

4. What is the weather usually like on his annual trip?

_____

5. In what place would the loser of the match finish the Championship?

_____

6. Why did Simon lean forward on the edge of his seat?

_____

Exercise 8 - On Holiday

Arthur finally sat munching on the sandwich he had been wanting to eat for hours. The morning had passed agreeably and he had all afternoon ahead of him to enjoy the lake. He moved the rudder towards him and let out the sails as he turned the vessel out into the lake. He would not return to the boathouse until tea-time.

When he did, he saw the familiar face of Mrs Foot, who owned the establishment he was staying in, a large guesthouse overlooking the water. He was surprised that in contrast to her usual neat presentation, she was wearing old clothes and green plastic gloves. He remembered her love of flowers and understood why.

As the sun set on a beautiful day in which the low temperature had masked the strength of the sun, he noticed his skin was itching with the beginnings of sunburn, and resolved to be more careful the next time he set out on the lake.

1.　What time is it at the start of the passage?

_____

2.　What is Arthur doing that afternoon?

_____

3.　How long does Arthur do this for?

_____

4.　What is Mrs Foot's occupation?

_____

5.　What was Mrs Foot doing?

_____

6.　What is the weather like at the end of the day?

_____

Exercise 9 - Everyday Difficulties

Ms Bridge hastily crossed the road, narrowly avoiding being hit by a car which beeped loudly, though she did not register the noise due to a profound affliction which meant her life was immersed in silence. This also meant that she found it difficult to buy the items she required, often asking shopkeepers to use a pen and notepad so she could find things.

She reached the supermarket to discover that there had been an accident: a trolley had been pushed through a window, which had resembled an open doorway in the strong sunlight. She carefully stepped around the broken glass.

She sometimes had a helper with her on these trips, a lad who lived across the street from her. However, on weekends he insisted that he could not miss his position in goal for the local team, so today Ms Bridge had ventured out alone.

She didn't have much to buy, so there had been no need to drive there, though her car couldn't carry much anyway as it was a two-seater coupé she had owned for twenty years. Anyway, it was just as well, as the vehicle had a dangerous tendency to take too long to stop.

1. Why does Ms Bridge find it difficult to go shopping?

_____

2. How do the shopkeepers help her?

_____

3. Why had a trolley been pushed through a window?

_____

4. Why couldn't the boy help at the weekend?

_____

5. What type of car does Ms Bridge drive?

_____

6. What part of the car is faulty?

_____

Exercise 10 - Stuck on the Mountain

It was getting dark and it was now clear that the four of them would have to spend another night on the mountain. Despite their best efforts, they had been unable to reach the campsite because heavy rain had driven debris down the mountainside, rendering the path impassable.

The night before, Molly, the leader of the group, insisted that attempts to climb down the steep descent into the valley should not be made at dusk, and that they should build a bivouac instead. Plans to explore the subterranean labyrinth near the youth hostel the next day had been abandoned. Molly thought bleakly that they might not even see the youth hostel again: weather conditions were getting worse.

Weather wasn't their only problem however: Molly's friend Paul had twisted his leg so badly that he was finding it difficult to walk. Morale was also low, and Jeff, another member of the group, was implacable, remaining pessimistic despite the jolly stories they shared to cheer themselves up.

1. Why can't the group get to the campsite?

_____

2. What was Molly's view on climbing down the hill at dusk?

_____

3. What had they planned to do the next day?

_____

4. Why do you think Molly thinks they might not see the hostel?

_____

5. What does 'Weather wasn't their only problem' refer to?

_____

6. What do you think 'implacable' means?

_____

Exercise 11 - The Team Dinner

Having won the local football tournament, the team had expected to have their celebratory meal that weekend, but it had been postponed to the first day of the working week. Their team manager, a local schoolteacher, was able to gain use of the hall in the old school where they had been pupils. This caused much amusement amongst the team. Jim, the goalkeeper, gave a wry smile to think that he would be having a party in the place where he studied many years before.

He had done well for himself. He now lived in a new 10-storey development on the outskirts of the town, which was incredibly modern and had fantastic views. He had been responsible for its design and had reserved one of the flats as soon as he had drawn up the plans. This he somewhat regretted as any small problem with the edifice was immediately pointed out by his neighbours, most notably the lack of adequate heating.

1. For what day is the meal planned?

_____

2. What does their manager decide to do?

_____

3. Why does Jim smile?

_____

4. What type of accommodation does Jim live in?

_____

5. What is Jim's job?

_____

6. What is a disadvantage of where he lives?

_____

Exercise 12 - A Long Drive

When the day finally came for Joanna to go on her long-planned trip, she was delayed as she had given the garage keys to her sister and had to go round to her house to fetch them before leaving. An hour later than planned, she set out to drive to Scotland. The journey would take nine hours, starting at her new home near London and arriving in the village where she grew up, in time for dinner.

She would stop once to see her uncle in Yorkshire, who had also relocated further south due to a job in nursing. She always enjoyed a visit to his house, a fact which was more to do with his culinary skills than the lengthy stories he always told.

In the first few hours of driving, progress was slow, but soon the traffic thinned and the miles went by quickly. Joanna liked driving alone, when she could steal time to appreciate a few choice albums that she carefully selected to bring along with her for the car stereo. In no time, she had forgotten London altogether.

1. Why could Joanna not leave on time?

_____

2. Where did Joanna live when she was young?

_____

3. What do Joanna and her uncle have in common?

_____

4. What is the main reason why Joanna enjoys visiting her uncle?

_____

5. Why does the drive take longer than expected at first?

_____

6. Why does Joanna enjoy driving by herself?

_____

Exercise 13 - Evacuation!

Seth had only been asleep for three hours when he was awoken by shouting outside his door and his cabin lurching dramatically to one side. He had only got to bed at midnight and had been hoping for a full night's sleep. What was the commotion?

He stumbled out into the corridor to be greeted by a scene of people in dressing gowns rushing in all directions and looking disorientated. An announcement was heard through a loud haler: "If anyone is still inside their cabin, please make your way to the nearest lifeboat up on deck." Evidently this was no drill: the crew were marching around rounding people up and there was a distinct sound of sloshing water coming from somewhere too close for comfort.

Suddenly panicking, Seth recalled leaving his diary in the communal dining room before going to bed. He glanced down the tilting corridor and noticed a shallow pool of water lapping at the dining room doors. No, he couldn't go back for it now. Suddenly wide awake, he grabbed a coat and clambered up the nearest staircase out onto the deck.

1. What time does Seth wake up?

_____

2. Who are the people in dressing gowns?

_____

3. Why does the story say that it was 'no drill'?

_____

4. Why does Seth panic?

_____

5. Why does Seth conclude it is not safe to go to the dining room?

_____

6. What do you think is happening to the ship?

_____

Exercise 14 - A Home Business

Sandra unpacked the equipment, placing each item neatly in a row before removing the instruction manual from its cellophane wrapper. The new computer certainly looked impressive, and should be for the hefty cost, she thought. The machine was necessary for her business, which had expanded vastly in the last six months. The huge quantity of customer orders coming had swamped her capacity, as well as the abilities of the jaded technology with which she had been running the business.

The model cars she imported from the Far East had proved unexpectedly popular, and soon she would have to recruit an assistant, if only to help repackage the toys and send them to customers on time. She was able to send them their orders within a fortnight, but this would have to be halved if she was to remain competitive. Still, it was a lucrative business, allowing her to earn twice what she had made as a policewoman.

1.   Why does Sandra expect the computer to perform well?

_____

2.   What does 'the machine' refer to?

_____

3.   What does 'jaded technology' refer to?

_____

4.   What is Sandra's business?

_____

5.   How quickly does she aim to be able to send orders in the future?

_____

6.   What is the meaning of the word 'lucrative'?

_____

Exercise 15 - The Visitor

Mr Motson opened the front door, and Theresa grinned at him.

"I brought you something to cheer you up," she said. Mr Motson sneezed and reached into his pocket for a handkerchief.

"That's very kind, Theresa," he croaked, "but I'm getting better now." He took the box Theresa handed him and peered at the lid. "Oh, how delightful!" he said, removing a coffee cream from its spot. He offered the box to Theresa, who scrutinised it carefully before taking some nougat in a dark coating.

Mr Motson stood back to let Theresa enter, and she looked around her with interest. There were books everywhere, filling the shelves that lined the walls, and stacked up in piles on the floor. The sun was bright outside, but although the windows were large and without shutters, the glass panes let in very little light. Theresa spotted a photograph of an elegant lady smiling at the camera.

"That's Edna," said Mr Motson. "She died long ago. And that's our daughter, Milly," he added, pointing to a picture of a young woman on the wall.

1. Who does 'the visitor' in the title refer to?

    _____

2. Why does Mr Motson need cheering up?

    _____

3. What does Theresa give to Mr Motson?

    _____

4. What is Mr Motson's hobby?

    _____

5. How do we know the windows are dirty?

    _____

6. Who do you think Edna is?

    _____

Exercise 16 - A Lazy Afternoon

Emma stretched out on her blanket and took another sandwich from the paper plate in front of her. She looked round her at her friends doing cartwheels on the grass and racing their bikes along the paths, narrowly avoiding crashing into couples strolling peacefully arm-in-arm. It was hot for the time of year and the sun was shining through the tender new leaves that were just emerging on the branches waving overhead.

Emma's best friend Pip handed her an apple and a glass of juice, and Emma lay back to relax. Emma and her friends were all in the same class at Hudson Grammar. Tomorrow, they'd be stuck in the classroom on the first school day of the week, but today, they could relax and enjoy themselves.

With a shock, Emma suddenly remembered: she hadn't done her homework! She would be in terrible trouble if she turned up to Mr Gibson's class without it. She sighed and started gathering her things together. The last thing she felt like doing was learning the dates of the kings and queens of England! What a disappointing end to a perfect afternoon.

1. Where is Emma?

_____

2. What time of year is it?

_____

3. What are Emma and her friends doing?

_____

4. Where does Emma know her friends from?

_____

5. Which day of the week is it?

_____

6. What subject does Mr Gibson teach?

_____

Exercise 17 - At the Races

Harry's eye was caught by a chestnut horse warming up by the side of the race track. Its rider's hair gleamed like gold in the sunlight. Harry's friend, Brenda, noticed his glance.

"That mare's a fast runner. I think the name is Double Dare," she said with a grin. "There's a notice over there that says 'For sale.'"

"Good spot. I'll think about it," replied Harry, wandering off towards the food stands.

Men in dress suits and ladies with extravagant hats were strolling around the VIP enclosures. He noticed one hat especially: it had a long peacock plume attached to its brim. The plume danced in the strong breeze, its iridescent blues and greens catching the light. The lady in the hat clamped a hand to it to stop it from blowing away.

"I'm going to do it, Brenda," Harry said, "I'm going to buy Double Dare."

Brenda whistled. "Are you sure?" she said. "You'll need double the £500 I paid for my old banger last year."

1. What colour is the horse Harry is looking at?

_____

2. How do we know its rider has blonde hair?

_____

3. What tells us that Double Dare is female?

_____

4. What do you think a 'plume' is?

_____

5. What is the weather like?

_____

6. How much money is Double Dare worth?

_____

Exercise 18 - A Narrow Escape

Nancy panted as they pedalled up the hillside. She looked at the surrounding Tuscan landscape and pulled over to the side of the road as a couple of locals on a motor scooter sputtered past, nattering away in Italian. Drops of sweat rolled down Nancy's face, and she admitted defeat, getting off her bike and pushing it towards the crown of the hill. She glanced behind her at David, his face red with effort, and remembered how much she'd enjoyed their wedding day last summer. This crazy trip had been his idea; slogging up hills on rickety bikes wasn't her idea of fun. She pulled a flask from her backpack and took a gulp of the refreshing transparent liquid it contained. She waved the flask at David, but he shook his head.

Suddenly, he gasped and Nancy saw a flash of green scales and a forked tongue flick out as something slithered past into the undergrowth, missing David's foot by a centimetre.

"That was a close call," said Nancy, shocked. "You'd have been dead in seconds if that thing had bitten you!"

1. In which country does the story take place?

_____

2. How do we know Nancy is hot?

_____

3. What is the relationship between Nancy and David?

_____

4. What type of holiday are they on?

_____

5. What is the liquid in Nancy's flask?

_____

6. What animal nearly bit David?

_____

Exercise 19 - St. Augustine's Tower

The sun was high overhead as Charlotte looked at the silhouette of the tower in front of her. There was a large clock face on its side, and Charlotte could make out the shape of a bell through its narrow, stone-framed windows. It made up the northern part of a rectangular, grey stone building with a golden cross perched on top.

Charlotte reached into her bag for some fruit. She felt its smooth, curved shape and peeled back the yellow skin before taking a big bite. She sat down on a grassy mound to wait for Jem, with her back resting against a slab of stone. She turned to read the writing inscribed on it: 'In loving memory of Mary, devoted wife and mother.' She made to stand up and gasped as she disturbed a small, black creature, which scuttled quickly out of sight. Her mother would have laughed at her: "They're perfectly harmless creatures and make beautiful webs. What a silly thing to be scared of!"

Charlotte glanced at her watch and frowned; she was beginning to wonder where Jem had got to. She was just reaching for her phone when Jem rushed up.

"I'm so sorry," he said, "I had to wait ages for a bus."

1. What time of day is it?

_____

2. What type of building is the tower part of?

_____

3. What type of fruit does Charlotte pull out of her bag?

_____

4. What does Charlotte lean against while waiting for Jem?

_____

5. What creature is Charlotte scared of?

_____

6. Why does Jem apologise to Charlotte?

_____

Exercise 20 - New York, New York!

The sky was a cloudless blue as Maddie walked down Fifth Avenue with a spring in her step. She could make out iconic landmarks amongst the skyscrapers that lined the streets, and could feel the buzz of Manhattan in the air. She smiled down at her new shoes, worn especially for her date with Gerry tonight. She loved the colour of the leather; it reminded her of the conkers she and her brothers used to collect back in England in the autumn and play with at school. She hoped Gerry would like them too.

It was the 31st of May today, exactly two months since they had first met in a downtown bar. Gerry was with a group of colleagues at the moment, celebrating the end of the semester and the start of the long school holidays. It would be ten weeks before they would be standing in front of a class again! He and Maddie had got talking and found that they had a lot in common, including the fact that they both had Dalmatians, which they walked in Central Park before work every morning. Maddie was looking forward to their date; they had tickets to the latest Spiderman movie and had arranged to meet at 6pm. Maddie couldn't wait!

1. How do we know Maddie is in a good mood?

_____

2. What colour are Maddie's shoes?

_____

3. On what date did Maddie and Gerry first meet?

_____

4. What is Gerry's job?

_____

5. What animal do Gerry and Maddie have in common?

_____

6. Where are Gerry and Maddie going on their date?

_____

Exercise 21 - Daydreaming

Padma looked out of the window. She could hear Miss Higgins droning on about the volcanoes in Costa Rica and the coffee crop in Nicaragua, but today she couldn't concentrate. She saw a plane flying overhead, a trail of cloud behind it, and wondered if it was heading to Delhi, where her grandparents lived. Soon, Padma would be there too. She imagined the heat on her skin, the smell of spices in the air and the gentle purring of her grandmother's marmalade cat as she played with her kittens.

She loved helping in the kitchen, especially on jam-making day. At other times, she would accompany her grandma to their favourite stall at the market where she could admire the big hooped earrings, chunky rings and bright bangles.

In the evenings, when it cooled down, they would play games in the garden. Padma liked the one where you had to hit balls under metal hoops on the lawn with a large wooden mallet. She hoped it wouldn't be monsoon season this time, but she'd better take her waterproof jacket just in case.

Just then the bell rang, and Padma stuffed her books into her bag, ready for the next lesson.

1. What subject is Miss Higgins teaching?

Geography

2. In which country do Padma's grandparents live?

(Delhi) India

3. What colour is Padma's grandmother's cat?

ginger

4. What sort of items are sold at Padma's favourite market stall?

Hooped eating, chuncky rings and bright bangles

5. What is the name of the outdoor game Padma likes?

croqua

6. What is the weather like in the monsoon season?

It rains

Exercise 22 - Starting a Novel

Geoff had wanted to write a novel for a long time, and now, as he had six months before he started his new job as a lawyer, he knew he had the opportunity. It was an important time in his life that he would always remember. Looking out of his window, he could see that the red and gold leaves were beginning to fall from the trees, and he could see cold mist on the fields. Soon it would be winter.

He walked up the narrow stairs of his house to the top floor, then climbed the stepladder up into the roof where his simple writing desk stood. Hours later, at precisely midnight, he put down his pen. The first, long chapter had taken twelve hours to produce.

He resolved to work at the same time the next day, but the basic lamp he relied on stopped working, and he had to stop early. Determined to write a chapter every single day of the week, he decided to start much earlier the next day.

Six months went by; a second book was started, and Geoff never became a lawyer...

1. What was the season when he began writing?

_____

2. Where do you think the writer lives?

_____

3. In what room in the house did he write?

_____

4. At what time did he start writing?

_____

5. Why could he not finish the second chapter the next day?

_____

6. How many chapters did Geoff want to write in one week?

_____

Exercise 23 - The Maths Class

The teacher frowned, but at last the class could begin. Joan was peeking round the door sheepishly. She was twenty minutes late, and mumbled an excuse about an alarm clock without batteries. She had missed a rail connection, she explained, and had had to take the bus. Her best friend, who was also her neighbour, smiled as Joan walked over to her usual desk. Their teacher, a stern man who was also the school's head, gestured for her to sit down quietly. Joan was the maths class's star pupil, and would soon catch up with the others.

The class was a double lesson, twice the length of the usual 45 minutes, so it was nearly lunchtime when it finished. The friends went away with vital homework for the big test that term, which was to take place just before the summer holidays.

1. How does Joan normally travel to school?

by train

2. Where does Joan's best friend live?

in the same neighbourhood

3. Who is better at maths, Joan or her friend?

Joan

4. How long is the maths class that day?

1 hour and 30 minutes

5. What is the teacher's main job title in the school?

school head

6. Which term is it?

summer term

Exercise 24 - Learning to Ride a Bike

The ice had finally thawed on the roads and flowers were beginning to be seen in the fields. It was a good day to learn how to ride a bike. Jeremy had been looking forward to this day, but he had to wait for his father to finish preparing the rusty old bike in the garage.

After an impatient hour, they were ready to start. His Dad had been busy all weekend, closing off the boundaries to the garden so the dog could not get out.

Jeremy's brother and sister could already ride. His eldest sibling, Gregory, had an extremely light bike, which left his sister, Jane, in the dust. Jane didn't care though because she won medals at school for sprinting. Once, she raced Gregory on his bike, running alongside, but they both crossed the finish line at the same time; she was that fast.

1. At what time of year does the story take place?

_____

2. Why was Jeremy impatient?

_____

3. What had Jeremy's father been doing in the garden?

_____

4. Who had the fastest bike?

_____

5. What is Jane very good at?

_____

6. Who won the race?

_____

Exercise 25 - The Lost Cabin

At first, the three children did not see the mysterious cabin when they came to the clearing in the wood. Indeed, only its roof could be seen from ground level and it could be accessed only by a steep set of steps leading down to its front door. It was the perfect place to stay the night, with a bedroom for each of them and one to spare for their rucksacks.

Jim and Elsie had brought bikes, while Chris had run behind. Elsie had painted hers a bright silver colour, while Jim's was a more demure shade. Jim got off his bike and, after a quick look at Chris, who looked chilly, handed him his jacket. They were all pleased to stop and rest.

After a good night's sleep, the friends scaled a nearby hill. Jim called down to Chris, who had stopped behind with Elsie to examine a molehill, asking for his jacket back. Chris liked the jacket so much that he gave it back reluctantly. Soon, they reached the top of the hill and surveyed the view. They had had an excellent couple of days and just managed to return home before the light disappeared.

1. What is strange about the cabin's position?

_____

2. How many rooms did the cabin have?

_____

3. Whose bike was a bolder colour?

_____

4. Why did Jim hand Chris his jacket?

_____

5. Who is closest to the top of the hill?

_____

6. At what time did they finally get home?

_____

Exercise 26 - The Secret Lake

Geoffrey the Yorkshire terrier had been missing all morning, and the siblings had ventured far into the fells. Finally, they came over the brow of a hill and saw him, happily drinking at the edge of a huge lake. What a clever dog! He wasn't always so clever: ever since he had been brought out to the countryside, away from the town's hustle and bustle, he couldn't helping running up into the hills, and he had already got lost at least three times. This wasn't good for the children's education; they had left their textbooks behind that morning because of the missing dog.

However, they were both excited by the discovery, and decided to come back the next day with an inflatable dinghy to go out onto the lake. In a way, it was the dog's fault that the boat capsized, though really they shouldn't have gone out in those conditions...

1. What were the children trying to do?

_____

2. Who found the lake?

_____

3. Where had they lived previously?

_____

4. What had the children been doing?

_____

5. What type of transport did they use the next day?

_____

6. What caused the accident the next day?

_____

Exercise 27 - Arranging a Party

Sam and Joanna were to be married the following year, so they threw a wonderful party in the summer. All their friends were there, as well as many colleagues from the newspaper in which Joanna wrote a regular article, and from the restaurant where Sam was a chef.

Originally, the couple had planned to rent a marquee and hold the party in a friend's garden, until they hit upon the idea of holding a waterborne event; the idea of sailing down the Thames was too good to resist. It was appropriate as the engaged couple had met whilst travelling overseas on a boating trip near Sam's birthplace. The highlight of the party was when a friend they had met on their travels arrived unexpectedly and recounted wonderful tales of their adventures abroad.

1.   What was the party celebrating?

_____

2.   What was Joanna's job?

_____

3.   How do we know the couple do not have a garden?

_____

4.   Where was the party held?

_____

5.   How do we know that Sam was born abroad?

_____

6.   Why do you think the friend did not say she was coming?

_____

Exercise 28 - Drone Racing Report

Join us from the other side of the world, in sunny Sydney! Today, we are looking at a brand new sport: drone racing.

Drones are small radio-controlled aircraft or quadcopters. They race along a complicated course at high speeds. Drone racers see the race from the first-person view by wearing goggles, so pilots see only what the drones see. A racing drone uses most of its energy for speed instead of hovering, which is the opposite of drones designed for photography. Drones designed for racing have four rotors pointing backwards, instead of the more usual downward configuration. Like the racers, spectators also wear goggles, so they can witness the race from the point of view of the racer they are following.

Drones can be bought quite cheaply, but the really fast ones are expensive. The drones speed at over 80 mph through incredible obstacles, making a race hugely exciting to watch.

After today's race, one of the pilots was kind enough to let me fly her drone. The level of skill and reaction speed needed is immense. Unfortunately, my drone did not make it round the course; I crashed on the second bend!

1. In which country did the race take place?

    _____

2. Can drone racers see their own drones whilst they are flying them?

    _____

3. Why would a racing drone not be good for photography?

    _____

4. In which direction do a normal drone's rotors point?

    _____

5. What is one of the problems with taking part in the sport?

    _____

6. Why do you think the commentator's drone crashed?

    _____

Exercise 29 - Sam's Day

As usual, Sam made her way down to the depot and, after saying 'good morning' to the conductor, she got behind the wheel of the number 73 and began her daily route, moving hundreds of passengers around the city. It was hard work, and there were another two days of work to go after today until she had some free time on Saturday.

She spent most of her weekends at home because she had very little desire to spend them driving around. However, this weekend she had to leave home, as she had suddenly realised the walls of her apartment were lacking decoration. She had decided to remedy this by visiting a local gallery to find something to liven the place up.

She wished she could go somewhere exciting and new, but she really didn't want to do any more driving! It was a pity because although her country had no coast, it did have some amazing mountains and valleys. Unfortunately, she was terrified of the tiny roads winding up the mountain's side. Sadly, most of her family lived on the other side of this mountain range, meaning she rarely saw them.

1. What is Sam's occupation?

_____

2. What day of the week is it?

_____

3. What does Sam want to buy this weekend?

_____

4. Why does Sam not want to do any more driving?

_____

5. What surrounds her country?

_____

6. What fear prevents Sam from seeing her family?

_____

Exercise 30 - Family Matters

Ryan's family were very important to him. He had older twin brothers and a younger sister, who had been born the year before, just after Christmas.

Ryan had moved away from home to go to college, but was visiting his family this weekend. Inconveniently, his phone wasn't working, so he walked into the town centre to find an internet café. They would get his message soon enough.

All his family were gathering to celebrate his mother's new job. She had been taking a break from work to study for a year, but said she was pleased to be getting back to the business of fixing people's teeth, at which she was extremely skilled.

1.   How many brothers does Ryan have?

There two

2.   In which season was his sister born?

winter winter

3.   How did Ryan manage to contact his family?

to celebrate his mothers new job

4.   Why was Ryan going home on this particular weekend?

_____

5.   What had his mother done in the past year, apart from study?

taking a break from fixing peoples teeth

6.   What is his mother's profession?

_____

Exercise 31 - Sibling Meet-Up

When Mark's sister, Josie, arrived at the front door, he was wearing plastic gloves covered in soap suds. He had not expected her to arrive so soon after lunch. Josie laughed; it was an unusual sight as she knew he did not do much housework of any kind. Things had changed a bit since he had moved into a new residence he had purchased the previous month. He had been able to move out of rented accommodation at last now that he had passed his veterinary qualification and had obtained a new job.

That afternoon, the two siblings sat happily in the garden. Josie sat immersed in a huge 1,000-page novel of which she had already read half, and by which she was thoroughly gripped.

It had been pouring with rain that morning so they were lucky to be sitting out in the garden. This had not stopped Mark doing lengths in the nearby open-air pool however. He loved the water and planned to swim across the English Channel one day.

1. What had Mark been doing when his sister arrived?

_____

2. What effect had Mark's new house had on him?

_____

3. Roughly how many pages of her book had Josie read?

_____

4. What does Josie think of her book?

_____

5. What was the weather like that afternoon?

_____

6. What had Mark been doing that morning?

_____

Exercise 32 - The Competitive Friend

Philippa leapt out of her red MINI and strode confidently over to the tennis courts. She was wearing a bright yellow shirt and shorts the same colour as her car. She loved all types of sport, and would cycle and play rugby when she wasn't playing tennis.

Her tennis partner, Terry, was not so competitive. He had arrived twenty minutes earlier on a rickety and poorly equipped bicycle, which was impossible to see at night. Seeing Philippa, he made a face which perfectly expressed his disappointment at his friend's lateness. Philippa apologised, and said that there had been terrible traffic, which was not true. Terry just shook his head and looked at his watch, vowing to himself that this time he would win their game of tennis.

Predictably, this did not happen, but he enjoyed it anyway. In any case, in his view, it was the taking part that counted. After the game, the two friends laughed and joked; in the end they had both really enjoyed the morning.

1. What colour were Philippa's shorts?

_____

2. What does Terry's bicycle lack?

_____

3. How does Terry feel about Philippa's arrival?

_____

4. What was the traffic like?

_____

5. Who usually wins their games of tennis?

_____

6. Who won the tennis match?

_____

Exercise 33 - Good Friends

Simon's friends, Priyanka and Konrad, lived near the centre of town in tiny, but well-located, apartments. They preferred to live in smaller places nearer the centre so they could enjoy concerts and other artistic events in the city. Konrad's place was particularly minute, but he loved it.

Simon had a larger place further from the centre, where he had space for a piano. He worked in a school, and his pupils always did well, but his real passion was music. He often enjoyed listening to obscure classical music until the early hours. He would regularly invite Priyanka and Konrad over to hear him play pieces which he had composed, and in turn they often invited him to their places to cook for him.

It was a great surprise when Simon announced that he planned to move overseas and take up music full time. His friends promised to visit him, but knew that they would never be able to replicate the great times they had had together.

1. What interest do the three friends have in common?

_____

2. Whose home is neither the smallest nor the biggest?

_____

3. Who lives furthest from the centre of town?

_____

4. What was Simon's job?

_____

5. When does Simon listen to classical pieces of music?

_____

6. Why can they not repeat the great times together?

_____

Exercise 34 - Holiday Delays

Looking at the flat tyre on her car, Helena scratched her head for a while, then, thinking of a solution, she took out her mobile phone from her pocket and rang her mother. She was going to need help if she was going to get to the ferry on time.

Helena's mum picked up the phone and, shortly afterwards, looked across at her husband, Robert, with some annoyance. She had to agree to take her daughter to the port. Robert was secretly pleased at this unexpected call; he had been worried about his daughter as she had only recently passed her driving test.

Helena's mother grabbed her coat and headed for the driveway, only to find that her car was missing. Of course! She had left it at the station. She would have to cycle the three miles to get it. It would be disastrous if Helena missed the ferry and had to cancel her holiday.

1. Why does Helena scratch her head?

_____

2. How had Helena planned to get to the ferry?

_____

3. What does Helena want her mother to do?

_____

4. Who is Robert in relation to Helena?

_____

5. What was Robert worried about?

_____

6. How did Helena's mother get to the station?

_____

Exercise 35 - A Complicated Class

Matt walked through the classroom door, smiling from ear to ear. He sat down in his usual place next to his best friend, who gave him a sweet. Matt's expression soon turned into a grimace. He hadn't noticed it was liquorice. His friend laughed, not understanding what the matter was.

Soon, the teacher began the class. She explained some complicated sums, followed by some even trickier geometry, which made Matt's head ache. He preferred history. Still, he would have to learn everything the teacher said because the test was at the start of next week. Perhaps his father would help him. He was an accountant and would have no problem explaining this tricky subject.

1. How does Matt feel at the beginning of the passage?

_____

2. Where does Matt normally sit?

_____

3. Why does Matt grimace?

_____

4. What subject is the lesson on?

_____

5. What day of the week is the test on?

_____

6. Why is it relevant that his father is an accountant?

_____

FIRST PAST THE POST®

Mini-Comprehensions

Inference

Non-Fiction

Exercise 1 - National Geographic

The National Geographic Society was founded in Washington D.C. in January 1888 by a group of 33 scientists and explorers to increase the spread of geographical knowledge. More than 120 years after its foundation, it is now one of the largest non-profit educational and scientific institutions in the world. Nine months after the society's foundation, the first issue of the *National Geographic Magazine* was published. It is published monthly, and has never missed an issue. It now covers a wide range of topical issues within geography, natural sciences, environmental conservation and world culture. It has become famous for its distinctive, yellow, block border, and its high standard and extensive use of dramatic photography, particularly on its front covers.

In 1975, a children's version of the magazine was launched under the name *National Geographic World,* but it adopted its current name, *National Geographic Kids*, 26 years later. The company also publishes over one hundred books a year for children. Beautiful photography, educational content and engaging activities are hallmarks of all of their publications aimed at children, and they have consequently won many Parents' Choice Gold Awards.

1. What was the original aim of the National Geographic Society?

_____

2. In which month was the first issue of the *National Geographic Magazine* published?

_____

3. How many issues are published in two years?

_____

4. Where does the magazine use photography?

_____

5. In what year did *National Geographic Kids* adopt its current name?

_____

6. How do we know that their children's publications are popular with parents?

_____

Exercise 2 - The Zoological Society of London

The Zoological Society of London (ZSL) is an international scientific and educational charity whose mission is to promote and achieve the conservation of animal species and their habitats around the world. It was founded in London in 1826 by Sir Stamford Raffles, Sir Humphry Davy, Robert Peel and various other naturalists and members of the nobility. Its original purpose was to create a collection of animals, a library and a museum, but it has now expanded to run two zoos in England, a research department and conservation projects in more than 50 countries around the world.

Over its almost 200-year history, ZSL London Zoo has been home to a number of famous animals: a golden eagle called Goldie, who escaped for 11 days in 1965; a gorilla called Guy, who regularly rescued sparrows when they flew into his enclosure; and an American black bear called Winnie, who was visited by A.A. Milne and his son, Christopher, and inspired the Winnie the Pooh books.

The charity is also involved in projects such as the One Less Campaign, which aims to make London free of single-use plastic bottles, in order to reduce plastic pollution in marine and freshwater environments.

1. Why is ZSL referred to as 'international'?

_____

2. Has ZSL's original purpose been achieved?

_____

3. Why were sparrows that flew into Guy's enclosure lucky?

_____

4. Why did A.A. Milne name his famous character Winnie?

_____

5. Why does ZSL want to reduce plastic pollution?

_____

6. What does the word 'zoological' mean?

_____

Exercise 3 - The London Planetarium

The London Planetarium was housed on Marylebone Road in London, next to Madame Tussauds, until 2006. The large, domed building is still there, but it is now part of Madame Tussauds. It used to provide shows about astronomy, taking people on tours of the universe as they lay on their backs and looked up at the night sky, which was projected onto its large dome.

The only planetarium currently open in London is now the Peter Harrison Planetarium at Greenwich, which opened in 2007. It was funded with a large grant from the Peter Harrison Foundation of £3.25 million. It is part of the National Maritime Museum, which runs awe-inspiring shows. These are similar to those that used to run at the London Planetarium, allowing the audience to explore the universe from the comfort of their own seats.

Most planetaria in the world are used for educational purposes, but some are used for training in celestial navigation. This is the skill of navigating by using the positions of the stars to help you, which is particularly helpful if you are at sea and have no landmarks to help you figure out your position.

1. Why does the audience lie on their backs in a planetarium?

_____

2. Why is the planetarium at Greenwich called the Peter Harrison Planetarium?

_____

3. What is a 'grant'?

_____

4. For what purpose is the Peter Harrison planetarium used?

_____

5. Why is it difficult to navigate at sea?

_____

6. In what jobs would celestial navigation be a helpful skill?

_____

Exercise 4 - Giant Pandas

The giant panda is easily recognisable by the black patches around its eyes, over its ears and across its body. Though it sometimes eats birds or rodents, its diet is 99% bamboo.

At one time, the giant panda lived in lowland areas of China, but because of farming, deforestation and other human development, it now lives in the mountains. The species is at risk and is dependent on conservation methods. Forty-nine live in zoos outside China, while 2,000 to 3,000 live in the wild. Fortunately, this number is on the rise. This has led the species to be reclassified from endangered to vulnerable.

The animal's colouring provides camouflage in its snowy habitat. The panda is active at the beginning and end of the day, venturing out at dawn and dusk, and so falling into the crepuscular category. Its digestion is unusual in that it can consume large quantities of bamboo each day. However, this provides it with limited energy, so it avoids sloping terrains and limits its activity in order to conserve energy.

1.   What does the giant panda rarely eat?

_____

2.   Who is responsible for the panda now only living in the mountains?

_____

3.   Why are pandas now classified as vulnerable and as not endangered?

_____

4.   What is the advantage of the panda's appearance?

_____

5.   What do pandas do in the middle of the day?

_____

6.   What is the disadvantage of the panda's diet of bamboo?

_____

Exercise 5 - The Forth Bridge

The Forth Bridge is in the east of Scotland, running from the west of Edinburgh City Centre. Construction on the bridge began in 1882 and lasted for eight years. With a total length of 8,094 feet, it was the longest single cantilever bridge in the world until 1917. It is now the second longest after the Quebec Bridge in Canada. The railway track on the Forth Bridge is elevated at 150 feet above the Firth of Forth, which is where many Scottish rivers meet the sea, and it weighs over 51,000 tons.

It was the first major structure in Britain to be constructed of steel, a modern material in comparison to the wrought iron of its contemporary, the Eiffel Tower. The use of steel was made possible after a process that could consistently produce high-quality steel was invented. About 4,600 workers were employed in its construction. It was dangerous work and 57 lives were lost, to whose memory a monument was built.

1. When did construction on the Forth Bridge finish?

_____

2. Where is the largest cantilever bridge in the world?

_____

3. What type of vehicles do we know pass over the Forth Bridge?

_____

4. What does the Forth Bridge pass over?

_____

5. What is the Eiffel Tower made of?

_____

6. What was done to remember the danger of building the bridge?

_____

Exercise 6 - Dirigibles

A dirigible, or hot air balloon, consists of an envelope of hot air with a gondola or wicker basket for passengers suspended underneath. The craft rises because it is lighter than air. This is because the air inside the balloon has a lower density than the colder air outside. Unlike airships, hot air balloons are not propelled or steered through the air, but simply drift in air currents.

The first hot air balloon flight took place in 1783 in France, with an unmanned flight lasting 10 minutes. Later that year, balloons were launched that carried animals, and finally humans. It was not until 1960 that modern hot air balloons with an on-board heat source were flown. Fuel tanks made of aluminium, stainless steel or titanium are now used.

A balloon has been successfully flown around the world by the Swiss psychiatrist, Bertrand Piccard. It took 19 days, 21 hours and 55 minutes. Balloons are able to fly at extremely high altitudes, but cannot rise above Earth's atmosphere.

1. In what year was the first hot air balloon flight with a human?

_____

2. What is the density of cold air compared to that of the air inside the balloon?

_____

3. What are airships able to do that hot air balloons cannot?

_____

4. What type of material are fuel tanks made of?

_____

5. Approximately how many weeks did the flight around the world take?

_____

6. What limits the altitude at which hot air balloons can fly?

_____

Exercise 7 - An Industrious Insect

Ants belong to the insect family of *Formicidae*, and to the order Hymenoptera, which also contains flying, yellow and black, striped insects that sting when frightened and sometimes produce honey. Ants are distinctive because of their narrow waists and jointed antennae, which are attached to the front of their heads.

They form colonies that range in size from a few dozen individuals to highly organised colonies comprising millions of individuals. These large colonies consist mostly of sterile, wingless females, which work as workers, soldiers or in another specialised role. There are also fertile males called drones, and one or two fertile females called queens. The ants work together as one entity to support the colony.

Ants live almost everywhere in the world, except for Antarctica, but they thrive best in the tropics. Human cultures make use of ants for various purposes, one of which is cuisine; ants are considered a delicacy in certain parts of the world. However, some species, such as the fire ant, which takes its name from the effect of its venom, are regarded as invasive species and are harmful to humans.

1. What other insects are closely related to the ant?

   _____

2. Are most ants in a large colony sterile or fertile?

   _____

3. How do we know that worker ants can't fly?

   _____

4. What sort of climate suits ants best?

   _____

5. What do humans in certain parts of the world use ants for?

   _____

6. What effect does the venom of the fire ant have?

   _____

Exercise 8 - Wake-Up Juice

Coffee is a brewed drink prepared from roasted coffee beans, which are the seeds of berries from *Coffea* plants. These plants are native to Madagascar, Mauritius, Kenya and Tanzania, but they have now been exported elsewhere. They are now grown in tropical climates across the world. The most common species are *C. arabica*, which makes up 75-80% of all coffee grown, and *C. canephora*, which makes up around 20% of all grown.

Coffee is slightly acidic and has a stimulating effect on humans because of its caffeine content. It is one of the most popular drinks in the world and can be prepared in a variety of ways. Black coffee is popular in America, hence its nickname 'Americano' in coffee shops around the world, whereas in the UK, the latte, which is Italian for milk, is more popular. Due to its energising effect, coffee is most often drunk with breakfast, or by commuters when they arrive at their place of work.

Coffeehouses, or cafés as they are known today, have been popular as meeting points in Europe since the early 17th century. Now, they are popular across the world and are a common sight on every British high street.

1. From which continent does coffee originate?

    _____

2. How do we know that *C. Arabica* is more popular than *C. canephora*?

    _____

3. Why is coffee referred to as 'wake-up juice' in the title?

    _____

4. What tells us that Americans prefer coffee without milk?

    _____

5. At what time of day is coffee most commonly drunk?

    _____

6. For roughly how long have cafés been popular in Europe?

    _____

Exercise 9 - The Lady with the Lamp

Florence Nightingale, who lived to the age of 90, was an English statistician, social reformer and the founder of modern nursing. She was born in 1820 in Italy and was named after the city of her birth. The following year, her family moved back to England and she grew up in Hampshire and Derbyshire.

From a young age, she wanted to devote her life to helping others and she announced her intention to be a nurse at the age of 24, despite social opposition and pressure for her to become a wife and mother. She started her career working at the Institute for the Care of Sick Gentlewomen in Harley Street in London in 1853.

She later became famous for her work caring for wounded soldiers in the Crimean War in the 1850s, where she trained and managed around 40 nurses. She reduced the death rate in the hospital in which she worked from 42% to 2%, mainly by making improvements in hygiene and ventilation. Nightingale believed that the high death rates were caused by insufficient nutrition, stale air and a lack of medical supplies, but this view was unpopular. She acquired her nickname 'The Lady with the Lamp' by doing regular rounds of the wards at night.

1. In which year did Florence Nightingale die?

_____

2. In which Italian city was Nightingale born?

_____

3. Why was it difficult for Nightingale to become a nurse?

_____

4. What was the main impact of Nightingale's work in the hospital in Crimea?

_____

5. Other than by improving hygiene and ventilation, how else did Nightingale believe the death rates could be reduced?

_____

6. What did Nightingale carry with her on her night-time rounds?

_____

Exercise 10 - Armadillos

Meaning 'little armoured one', armadillos are named for their distinctive plated armour. All but one species of armadillo live in South America. They can move very quickly, but are only active for short periods of the day. Giant armadillos sleep for 18 hours per day. The nine-banded armadillo is unusual because it regularly has identical quadruplets.

The armadillo's worst enemy is cold temperatures because its body has poor fat stores; therefore, cold weather conditions can have a dire effect on armadillo populations. They vary hugely in size from as small as six inches to as large as six feet long.

They have poor eyesight, using their sense of smell to hunt prey such as beetles, ants and termites. They use their long snouts and sticky tongues to extract prey from their burrows. When threatened, armadillos often roll themselves into a ball, rather like a certain prickly creature found in England.

1. Are armadillos found in the wild outside South America?

_____

2. Why do the offspring of the nine-banded armadillo often look similar to each other?

_____

3. What can cause the number of armadillos to decrease?

_____

4. How many times larger is the largest armadillo than the smallest?

_____

5. What part of their body do they rely on to find prey?

_____

6. What other animal is referred to at the end of the text?

_____

Exercise 11 - Chameleons

A type of lizard, the chameleon is known for its ability to change colour to match its environment. Its skin has a superficial layer that contains pigments. It uses this for camouflage, but mainly for signalling to other chameleons.

The creatures are found in many areas of the world and are often kept as pets. Chameleons have a prehensile tail, meaning it can be used to hold onto objects. Their eyes can also move independently.

Given this suite of extraordinary features, it is perhaps surprising that the name 'chameleon' comes simply from the Greek words for 'on the ground' and 'lion'. Can you think of a better name for it?

1. Why are chameleons sometimes difficult to see?

_____

2. What is the main purpose of changing colour for a chameleon?

_____

3. Are chameleons dangerous to humans?

_____

4. What unusual part of their body can chameleons use to grasp objects?

_____

5. Why can a chameleon look in two directions at once?

_____

6. What does the text say is surprising?

_____

Exercise 12 - The World's Highest City

La Paz is the highest city in the world. Its full name means 'Our Lady of the Peace'. It is not the largest city in its country, coming after Santa Cruz and El Alto, but it is the capital of Bolivia. It is also the third most populous city in Bolivia.

Due to its altitude, it has a peculiar climate: it rains in summer and is dry in the winter. The city is culturally divided, with the richest people living in the lower central areas of the city, middle-class residents living in high-rise blocks, and the poorest living in simple houses in the surrounding hills.

La Paz has a rich history: it has been home to the Incas and later, the Spanish settlers. Recent political stability means the economy has improved and La Paz is now home to some of the most important universities in Bolivia, and also the most important museums.

1. What is La Paz more known for, its size or status?

_____

2. What would you say the seasonal pattern of rain is like compared to England?

_____

3. Which residents live at the lowest altitude?

_____

4. What evidence is there that La Paz is an old city?

_____

5. Has the political situation improved or worsened in recent years?

_____

6. How do we know that La Paz is a centre of culture?

_____

Exercise 13 - The Transistor Radio

A transistor radio is a small portable radio that uses transistor-based circuitry. The transistor radio was invented seven years after the invention of the transistor, which took place in 1947.

They were to become the most popular electronic communication device in history, with billions manufactured during the 1960s and 1970s. Their pocket-size shape sparked a change in popular music listening habits, allowing people to listen to music anywhere they went.

Beginning in the 1980s, however, transistor radios were superseded by devices with higher audio quality, such as portable CD players, cassette players, mp3 players, and today, smartphones.

1. When was the transistor radio invented?

_____

2. For how many decades were transistor radios popular?

_____

3. Why did people start to listen to more music after transistor radios were invented?

_____

4. What was the advantage of newer technology in 1980s?

_____

5. Why are transistor radios less popular now?

_____

6. What do people use now instead of transistor radios?

_____

Exercise 14 - Hang Gliding

Hang gliders have an aluminium frame that is covered with sailcloth to form a wing. The pilot usually sits in a harness beneath the wing. They rely on currents of air rather than a motor for power.

Early hang gliders could take short flights after being launched from a hill, but modern designs can fly for hours, climbing to thousands of feet above the ground and travelling for hundreds of kilometres. Invented in China, they started off as large kites, but eventually the kite strings were removed and the person became attached to the aircraft.

The pilot is able to control the craft by using a triangular frame, which increases the speed of the glider if pulled. Early hang gliders were often unsafe, but now a parachute is incorporated into the harness, which can transport the pilot safely to earth if necessary.

1. What part of a hang glider is made of material that could be found on a boat?

_____

2. Where is a hang glider's motor situated?

_____

3. To what toy is a hang glider similar?

_____

4. How many sides does a hang glider's control-frame have?

_____

5. As well as direction, what can a pilot control?

_____

6. What can a pilot use in an emergency?

_____

Exercise 15 - Giant Squids

Giant squids are deep-ocean-dwelling creatures that can grow to a tremendous size. Their ability to grow to such huge sizes can be accounted for by their habitat, deep in the sea. Recent estimates put their maximum size at 13m for females and 10m for males, measuring from the rear fins to the tips of the pair of long tentacles. There have even been claims that specimens measuring 20m or more have been sighted, but these have not been scientifically validated. Since their bodies have elastic properties, their dimensions remain uncertain.

They are extraordinary creatures, and they also have the largest eyes of any animal, at 10 inches in diameter. They are related to mussels and other molluscs. The number of giant squid species is under debate, but recent genetic research suggests that they are all the same species.

In 2004, Japanese researchers took the first images of a giant squid in its natural habitat, and not until July 2012 was an adult filmed in its natural habitat for the first time.

1. Why can squids grow so large?

_____

2. Which sex of giant squid is larger?

_____

3. Why can't scientists be certain of a squid's length?

_____

4. Is a giant squid a fish?

_____

5. How many species of giant squid are there?

_____

6. Why do you think giant squids were not filmed in their natural habitat until 2012?

_____

Answers & Explanations

English: Mini-Comprehensions

Inference

Book 1

Many candidates will provide answers that are not exact, word-for-word matches to those provided in the following mark scheme. If the candidate's answer is reasonable, and/or a very close match to that suggested, it should be marked correct. This is a consequence of standard format inference questions: there is often more than one valid way to infer the answer. Every effort has been made to cater for the most common, expected answers.

Question	Answer	Explanation
1	on a cliff/clifftop/at the coast/seaside	Inferred from the line: 'Miranda strode out along the clifftop path... Wild waves crashed against the rocks below her...'
2	spring	Inferred from the line: 'Budding daffodils were bursting forth...and blossom itched to erupt...'
3	a dog	Inferred from the line: '...Miranda leant down and unclipped Max's lead from his collar.'
4	Max splashed them with mud.	Inferred from the line: 'He splashed recklessly through muddy puddles, spraying a nearby family...'
5	afternoon	Inferred from the line: '...sunset was not for another couple of hours.'
6	three	Inferred from the line: 'For the third year running, Max was refusing to grow up...'

Fiction - Exercise 2 - Café Rush Hour, page 3

Question	Answer	Explanation
1	a waiter	Inferred from the line: 'Phillip dashed as quickly as he could back to the kitchen...expertly balancing a tower of used coffee cups and plates...'
2	Wednesday	Inferred from the line: 'Midweek was always the busiest time here...'
3	The weather was nice.	Inferred from the line: '...today was especially busy:...people enjoyed basking in the warm afternoon sun...'
4	2pm	Inferred from the line: '...it began to chime four o'clock; he had only been on shift for two hours...'
5	He enjoyed serving his regular customers.	Inferred from the line: '...he loved serving all his regular customers their favourite afternoon treats...'
6	6pm	Inferred from the line: '...the clock signalled six o'clock and he ushered the last customers out...'

Fiction - Exercise 3 - Travel Plans, page 4

Question	Answer	Explanation
1	a bookshop	Inferred from the line: '...the man searching through the shelves... what kind of travel-guide he was looking for...'
2	He was browsing travel guides/in the travel bookshop.	Inferred from the line: '...the man searching through the shelves... what kind of travel-guide he was looking for...'
3	new/unusual	Inferred from the line: '"That's a novel way of doing things,"... Never had she encountered...'
4	She worked in the bookshop.	Inferred from the line: '...Megan thought it was time that she went over to offer some help.'
5	Central America	Inferred from the line: '...he settled on a book about Belize... flights to Central America were expensive...'
6	Asia and South America	Inferred from the line: '...previous adventures to Nepal and Brazil.'

Fiction - Exercise 4 - The Final Ascent, page 5

Question	Answer	Explanation
1	a mountain/hill	Inferred from the line: 'The rocky ground began to slope even more steeply... the bitter-cold, biting winds and exhausting climb...'
2	one week	Inferred from the line: 'The expedition was on its final day of a three-day ascent, and was expected to take a similar amount of time to return...'
3	a charity	Inferred from the line: '...the amount of money the team had succeeded in raising for Unicef... Unicef had helped each of them at some point in their lives.'
4	They would share the success of the expedition.	Inferred from the line: '...their current total was likely to increase once they shared the success of their climb with everyone back home.'
5	Unicef had helped them all/they had all benefitted from Unicef.	Inferred from the line: 'Everyone in the group had a personal reason to raise money, as Unicef had helped each of them at some point in their lives.'
6	six	Inferred from the line: '...they looked back down the slope at the six tracks of footprints snaking away...'

Fiction - Exercise 5 - A New Restaurant, page 6

Question	Answer	Explanation
1	Italian	Inferred from the line: '...yet another pizza dough... a similar number of pasta dishes... had worked in several top restaurants across Italy.'
2	6pm	Inferred from the line: '...it was only 7.30pm! ...the restaurant had opened an hour and a half ago...'
3	It had opened only recently/six months ago.	Inferred from the line: 'The restaurant was the most popular in town, despite opening only six months ago...'
4	the experience of the head chef	Inferred from the line: '...this was expected given the extensive experience of the head chef...'
5	They would bring more people into the area/more custom.	Inferred from the line: '...it was only a matter of time before they began to receive glowing reviews in national newspapers as well, which would surely bring many more people into the area.'
6	to bring good food to people at affordable prices	Inferred from the line: '...the head chef's main motivation for her work was to allow even more people to enjoy good, fresh and delicious food for reasonable prices.'

Fiction - Exercise 6 - A Long Plane Journey, page 7

Question	Answer	Explanation
1	the airport	Inferred from the line: 'The plane...hurtled down the runway for take-off.'
2	They were reluctant/unhappy about the long flight/ uncomfortable.	Inferred from the line: '...as they resigned themselves to the cramped seats for the next eleven hours...'
3	11 hours	Inferred from the line: '...they resigned themselves to the cramped seats for the next eleven hours...'
4	to find out why the alarm had gone off	Inferred from the line: 'The captain hurriedly checked all screens and dials for error messages... after checking every last possibility, the captain called off the alarm...'
5	It had been a false alarm.	Inferred from the line: '...informed the passengers calmly that there was no need to panic and that it had been a false alarm.'
6	The flight had been scary (or similar).	Inferred from the line: 'Panic ensued... everyone disembarked, much shaken from the flight's events...'

Fiction - Exercise 7 - A Day Out at Wimbledon, page 8

Question	Answer	Explanation
1	tennis	Inferred from the line: '...marching out onto court, determinedly carrying their rackets over their shoulders. The ball boys and girls were rolling the bright yellow balls along the sides of the court.'
2	The match is about to begin.	Inferred from the line: 'All preparations were in full swing and the tension was rising.'
3	once a year	Inferred from the line: 'Simon always enjoyed his annual trip to Wimbledon...'
4	nice/good/sunny/fine	Inferred from the line: '...the sun was out...'
5	second	Inferred from the line: '...whoever won would win the Championship.'
6	He was excited/tense/anticipating the start of the match.	Inferred from the line: 'Simon leaned forward on the edge of his seat as the match began...'

Fiction - Exercise 8 - On Holiday, page 9

Question	Answer	Explanation
1	lunchtime/noon/midday	Inferred from the line: 'The morning had passed agreeably and he had all afternoon ahead of him to enjoy the lake.'
2	sailing	Inferred from the line: 'He moved the rudder towards him and let out the sails as he turned the vessel out into the lake.'
3	the rest of the afternoon	Inferred from the line: 'He would not return to the boathouse until tea-time.'
4	She owns a hotel.	Inferred from the line: '...Mrs Foot, who owned the establishment he was staying in, a large guesthouse...'
5	gardening	Inferred from the line: '...she was wearing old clothes and green plastic gloves. He remembered her love of flowers and understood why.'
6	sunny but cold	Inferred from the line: '...the low temperature had masked the strength of the sun.'

Fiction - Exercise 9 - Everyday Difficulties, page 10

Question	Answer	Explanation
1	She can't hear/is deaf.	Inferred from the line: '...due to a profound affliction which meant her life was immersed in silence.'
2	They write on a notepad.	Inferred from the line: '...often asking shopkeepers to use a pen and notepad so she could find things.'
3	A window had looked like an open doorway.	Inferred from the line: '...a trolley had been pushed through a window, which had resembled an open doorway in the strong sunlight.'
4	He was playing football/sport/as goalie.	Inferred from the line: '...he could not miss his position in goal for the local team...'
5	an old sports/two-seater car	Inferred from the line: '...her car couldn't carry much anyway as it was a two-seater coupé she had owned for twenty years.'
6	the brakes	Inferred from the line: 'Anyway, it was just as well, as the vehicle had a dangerous tendency to take too long to stop.'

Fiction - Exercise 10 - Stuck on the Mountain, page 11

Question	Answer	Explanation
1	The path is blocked by a landslide.	Inferred from the line: '...heavy rain had driven debris down the mountainside, rendering the path impassable.'
2	It was too dangerous.	Inferred from the line: '...insisted that attempts to climb down the steep descent into the valley should not be made at dusk...'
3	go caving/ underground/ explore the labyrinth	Inferred from: 'Plans to explore the subterranean labyrinth near the youth hostel the next day had been abandoned.'
4	The weather was getting worse.	Inferred from the line: 'Molly thought bleakly that they might not see the youth hostel again: weather conditions were getting worse.'
5	Paul's injury/ twisted leg	Inferred from the line: 'Molly's friend Paul had twisted his leg so badly that he was finding it difficult to walk.'
6	refusing to be cheered up	Inferred from the line: '...remaining pessimistic despite the jolly stories they shared to cheer themselves up.'

Fiction - Exercise 11 - The Team Dinner, page 12

Question	Answer	Explanation
1	Monday	Inferred from the line: '...the first day of the working week.'
2	use a school hall as the venue for their celebratory dinner	Inferred from the line: '...able to gain use of the hall in the old school...'
3	The location amuses him/he will be relaxing where he once studied.	Inferred from the line: '...to think that he would be having a party in the place where he studied...'
4	a flat/high-rise flat/ tower block	Inferred from the line: 'He now lived in a new 10-storey development on the outskirts of the town, which was incredibly modern and had fantastic views.'
5	an architect	Inferred from the line: 'He had been responsible for its design and... had drawn up the plans.'
6	Neighbours criticise the design of the building (due to its heating problems).	Inferred from the line: '...any small problem with the edifice was immediately pointed out by his neighbours, most notably the lack of adequate heating.'

Fiction - Exercise 12 - A Long Drive, page 13

Question	Answer	Explanation
1	Her car was locked in the garage.	Inferred from the line: '...she had given the garage keys to her sister...'
2	a village in Scotland	Inferred from the line: '...she set out to drive to Scotland. ...arriving in the village where she grew up...'
3	They both moved further south.	Inferred from the line: '...who had also relocated further south...'
4	good food/Her uncle is a good cook.	Inferred from the line: 'She always enjoyed a visit to his house, a fact which was more to do with his culinary skills...'
5	bad traffic	Inferred from the line: '...progress was slow, but soon the traffic thinned...'
6	She can listen to her own music.	Inferred from the line: '...she could steal time to appreciate a few choice albums...'

Fiction - Exercise 13 - Evacuation!, page 14

Question	Answer	Explanation
1	3am	Inferred from the line: 'Seth had only been asleep for three hours… He had only got to bed at midnight…'
2	other passengers	Inferred from the line: '…people in dressing gowns rushing in all directions and looking disorientated. …"If anyone is still inside their cabin, please make your way to the nearest lifeboat up on deck."'
3	The crew were evacuating people/ there was water on board.	Inferred from the line: 'Evidently this was no drill: the crew were marching around rounding people up and there was a distinct sound of sloshing water…'
4	He remembers leaving his diary in the dining room.	Inferred from the line: 'Suddenly panicking, Seth recalled leaving his diary in the communal dining room before going to bed.'
5	He sees water lapping at the door.	Inferred from the line: '…noticed a shallow pool of water lapping at the dining room doors.'
6	It's sinking.	Inferred from the line: '"…make your way to the nearest lifeboat…" …a distinct sound of sloshing water…'

Fiction - Exercise 14 - A Home Business, page 15

Question	Answer	Explanation
1	It was expensive.	Inferred from the line: 'The new computer certainly looked impressive, and should be for the hefty cost…'
2	Sandra's new computer	Inferred from the line: 'The new computer certainly looked impressive… The machine was necessary…'
3	her old computer	Inferred from the line: '…customer orders coming had swamped her capacity, as well as the abilities of the jaded technology…'
4	She sells model cars.	Inferred from the line: 'The model cars she imported from the Far East had proved unexpectedly popular…'
5	in a week	Inferred from the line: 'She was able to send them their orders within a fortnight, but this would have to be halved…'
6	profitable (or synonym)	Inferred from the line: '…it was a lucrative business, allowing her to earn twice what she had made…'

Fiction - Exercise 15 - The Visitor, page 16

Question	Answer	Explanation
1	Theresa	Inferred from the line: 'Mr Motson opened the front door, and Theresa grinned at him.'
2	He has a cold.	Inferred from the line: 'Mr Motson sneezed and reached into his pocket for a handkerchief. "That's very kind, Theresa," he croaked…'
3	a box of chocolates	Inferred from the line: '…removing a coffee cream from its spot. He offered the box to Theresa, who scrutinised it carefully before taking some nougat in a dark coating.'
4	reading	Inferred from the line: 'There were books everywhere, filling the shelves that lined the walls, and stacked up in piles on the floor.'
5	Although they are large and have no shutters, they are letting in hardly any light, even though it's sunny outside.	Inferred from the line: 'The sun was bright outside, but although the windows were large and without shutters, the glass panes let in very little light.'
6	Mr Motson's wife/ Milly's mother	Inferred from the line: '"That's Edna," said Mr Motson. "She died long ago. And that's our daughter, Milly," he added…'

Fiction - Exercise 16 - A Lazy Afternoon, page 17

Question	Answer	Explanation
1	in a park	Inferred from the line: '… her friends doing cartwheels on the grass and racing their bikes along the paths, narrowly avoiding crashing into couples strolling peacefully arm-in-arm.'
2	spring	Inferred from the line: '…the sun was shining through the tender new leaves that were just emerging on the branches waving overhead.'
3	having a picnic	Inferred from the line: 'Emma stretched out on her blanket and took another sandwich from the paper plate in front of her.'
4	(Hudson Grammar) School	Inferred from the line: 'Emma and her friends were all in the same class at Hudson Grammar.'
5	Sunday	Inferred from the line: 'Tomorrow, they'd be stuck in the classroom on the first school day of the week…'
6	history	Inferred from the line: '…if she turned up to Mr Gibson's class without it. ….The last thing she felt like doing was learning the dates of the kings and queens of England!'

Fiction - Exercise 17 - At the Races, page 18

Question	Answer	Explanation
1	(chestnut/reddish) brown	Inferred from the line: 'Harry's eye was caught by a chestnut horse...'
2	The hair is described as gleaming like gold.	Inferred from the line: 'Its rider's hair gleamed like gold in the sunlight.'
3	Brenda refers to her as a mare.	Inferred from the line: '"That mare's a fast runner."'
4	a feather	Inferred from the line: '...it had a long peacock plume attached to its brim. The plume danced in the strong breeze...'
5	windy	Inferred from the line: 'The plume danced in the strong breeze... The lady in the hat clamped a hand to it to stop it from blowing away.'
6	£1,000	Inferred from the line: '"I'm going to buy Double Dare." Brenda whistled. "Are you sure?" she said. "You'll need double the £500 I paid for my old banger last year."'

Fiction - Exercise 18 - A Narrow Escape, page 19

Question	Answer	Explanation
1	Italy	Inferred from the line: 'She looked at the surrounding Tuscan landscape... nattering away in Italian.'
2	Drops of sweat are rolling down her face.	Inferred from the line: 'Drops of sweat rolled down Nancy's face...'
3	husband and wife	Inferred from the line: 'She glanced behind her at David, his face red with effort, and remembered much she'd enjoyed their wedding day last summer.'
4	a cycling holiday	Inferred from the line: 'This crazy trip had been his idea; slogging up hills on rickety bikes wasn't her idea of fun.'
5	water	Inferred from the line: 'She pulled a flask from her backpack and took a gulp of the refreshing transparent liquid it contained.'
6	a snake	Inferred from the line: 'Nancy saw a flash of green scales and a forked tongue flick out as something slithered past...'

Question	Answer	Explanation
1	midday/noon	Inferred from the line: 'The sun was high overhead…'
2	a church	Inferred from the line: 'There was a large clock face on its side, and Charlotte could make out the shape of a bell through its narrow, stone-framed windows. It made up the northern part of a rectangular, grey stone building with a golden cross perched on top.'
3	a banana	Inferred from the line: 'She felt its smooth, curved shape and peeled back the yellow skin before taking a big bite.'
4	a gravestone	Inferred from the line: '…with her back resting against a slab of stone. She turned to read the writing inscribed on it: 'In loving memory of Mary, devoted wife and mother.''
5	spiders	Inferred from the line: ''They're perfectly harmless creatures and make beautiful webs. What a silly thing to be scared of!''
6	He is late to meet Charlotte.	Inferred from the line: '…she was beginning to wonder where Jem had got to. She was just reaching for her phone when Jem rushed up. "I'm so sorry," he said, "I had to wait ages for a bus."'

Fiction - Exercise 20 - New York, New York!, page 21

Question	Answer	Explanation
1	She has a spring in her step.	Inferred from the line: '…Maddie walked down Fifth Avenue with a spring in her step.'
2	reddish brown/ chestnut/burgundy	Inferred from the line: 'She smiled down at her new shoes… She loved the colour of the leather; it reminded her of the conkers…'
3	31st March	Inferred from the line: 'It was the 31st of May today, exactly two months since they had first met…'
4	a teacher	Inferred from the line: '…celebrating the end of the semester and the start of the long school holidays. It would be ten weeks before they would be standing in front of a class again!'
5	dogs	Inferred from the line: '…they had a lot in common, including the fact that they both had Dalmatians, which they walked in Central Park before work every morning.'
6	the cinema	Inferred from the line: 'Maddie was looking forward to their date; they had tickets to the latest Spiderman movie…'

Fiction - Exercise 21 - Daydreaming, page 22

Question	Answer	Explanation
1	**geography**	Inferred from the line: 'She could hear Miss Higgins droning on about the volcanoes in Costa Rica and the coffee crop in Nicaragua…'
2	**India**	Inferred from the line: '…wondered if it was heading to Delhi, where her grandparents lived.'
3	**ginger**	Inferred from the line: '…the gentle purring of her grandmother's marmalade cat as she played with her kittens.'
4	**jewellery**	Inferred from the line: '…their favourite stall at the market where she could admire the big hooped earrings, chunky rings and bright bangles.'
5	**croquet**	Inferred from the line: 'Padma liked the one where you had to hit balls under metal hoops on the lawn with a large wooden mallet.'
6	**rainy**	Inferred from the line: 'She hoped it wouldn't be monsoon season this time, but she'd better take her waterproof jacket just in case.'

Fiction - Exercise 22 - Starting a Novel, page 23

Question	Answer	Explanation
1	**autumn**	Inferred from the line: '…the red and gold leaves were beginning to fall from the trees, and he could see cold mist on the fields. Soon it would be winter.'
2	**in the countryside**	Inferred from the line: '…he could see cold mist on the fields.'
3	**attic/loft**	Inferred from the line: 'He walked up the narrow stairs of his house to the top floor, then climbed the stepladder up into the roof…'
4	**12pm/midday/ noon**	Inferred from the line: '…at precisely midnight, he put down his pen. The first, long chapter had taken twelve hours to produce.'
5	**He did not have enough light/his light broke.**	Inferred from the line: '…the basic lamp he relied on stopped working, and he had to stop early.'
6	**seven**	Inferred from the line: 'Determined to write a chapter every single day of the week…'

Fiction - Exercise 23 - The Maths Class, page 24

Question	Answer	Explanation
1	**by train**	Inferred from the line: 'She had missed a rail connection...'
2	**in the house next door to Joan**	Inferred from the line: 'Her best friend, who was also her neighbour...'
3	**Joan**	Inferred from the line: 'Joan was the maths class's star pupil...'
4	**one and a half hours/90 minutes**	Inferred from the line: 'The class was a double lesson, twice the length of the usual 45 minutes...'
5	**headmaster**	Inferred from the line: 'Their teacher, a stern man who was also the school's head...'
6	**the summer term**	Inferred from the line: '...vital homework for the big test that term, which was to take place just before the summer holidays.'

Fiction - Exercise 24 - Learning to Ride a Bike, page 25

Question	Answer	Explanation
1	**spring**	Inferred from the line: 'The ice had finally thawed on the roads and flowers were beginning to be seen in the fields.'
2	**He had to wait for the bike to be fixed/prepared.**	Inferred from the line: 'Jeremy had been looking forward to this day, but he had to wait for his father to finish preparing the rusty old bike in the garage.'
3	**closing off the garden/building a wall or fence to keep the dog in**	Inferred from the line: 'His Dad had been busy all weekend, closing off the boundaries to the garden so the dog could not get out.'
4	**Gregory**	Inferred from the line: 'His eldest sibling, Gregory, had an extremely light bike, which left his sister, Jane, in the dust.'
5	**running/sprinting**	Inferred from the line: '...she won medals at school for sprinting.'
6	**It was a tie or draw/neither Jane nor Gregory won.**	Inferred from the line: '...she raced Gregory on his bike, running alongside, but they both crossed the finish line at the same time...'

Fiction - Exercise 25 - The Lost Cabin, page 26

Question	Answer	Explanation
1	It was below ground level/low down/down a slope.	Inferred from the line: '…only its roof could be seen from ground level and it could be accessed only by a steep set of steps leading down to its front door.'
2	four	Inferred from the line: '…a bedroom for each of them and one to spare for their rucksacks.'
3	Elsie's	Inferred from the line: 'Elsie had painted hers a bright silver colour, while Jim's was a more demure shade.'
4	Chris looked cold.	Inferred from the line: '…after a quick look at Chris, who looked chilly, handed him his jacket.'
5	Jim	Inferred from the line: 'Jim called down to Chris, who had stopped behind with Elsie…'
6	at sunset	Inferred from the line: '…just managed to return home before the light disappeared.'

Fiction - Exercise 26 - The Secret Lake, page 27

Question	Answer	Explanation
1	find their dog	Inferred from the line: 'Geoffrey the Yorkshire terrier had been missing all morning, and the siblings had ventured far into the fells.'
2	Geoffrey	Inferred from the line: '…they came over the brow of a hill and saw him, happily drinking at the edge of a huge lake. What a clever dog!'
3	in a town/city	Inferred from the line: '…ever since he had been brought out to the countryside, away from the town's hustle and bustle…'
4	studying	Inferred from the line: '…they had left their textbooks behind that morning because of the missing dog.'
5	a boat	Inferred from the line: '…decided to come back the next day with an inflatable dinghy to go out onto the lake.'
6	bad weather	Inferred from the line: '…though really they shouldn't have gone out in those conditions…'

Fiction - Exercise 27 - Arranging a Party, page 28

Question	Answer	Explanation
1	Sam and Joanna's engagement	Inferred from the line: 'Sam and Joanna were to be married the following year, so they threw a wonderful party…'
2	a journalist	Inferred from the line: '…as well as many colleagues from the newspaper in which Joanna wrote a regular article an article…'
3	They were planning to hold the party in a friend's garden.	Inferred from the line: '…the couple had planned to rent a marquee and hold the party in a friend's garden…'
4	on a boat	Inferred from the line: '…they hit upon the idea of holding a waterborne event; the idea of sailing down the Thames was too good to resist.'
5	The couple met whilst travelling near his birthplace.	Inferred from the line: '…the engaged couple had met whilst travelling overseas on a boating trip near Sam's birthplace.'
6	She wanted to surprise them.	Inferred from the line: 'The highlight of the party was when a friend they had met on their travels arrived unexpectedly…'

Fiction - Exercise 28 - Drone Racing Report, page 29

Question	Answer	Explanation
1	Australia	Inferred from the line: 'Join us from the other side of the world, in sunny Sydney!'
2	no	Inferred from the line: 'Drone racers see the race from the first-person view by wearing goggles…'
3	It does not hover.	Inferred from the line: 'A racing drone uses most of its energy for speed instead of hovering, which is the opposite of drones designed for photography.'
4	downwards	Inferred from the line: 'Drones designed for racing have four rotors pointing backwards, instead of the more usual downward configuration.'
5	It can be expensive.	Inferred from the line: 'Drones can be bought quite cheaply, but the really fast ones are expensive.'
6	poor skill of the driver	Inferred from the line: 'The level of skill and reaction speed needed is immense. Unfortunately, my drone did not make it round the course…'

Fiction - Exercise 29 - Sam's Day, page 30

Question	Answer	Explanation
1	**a bus driver**	Inferred from the line: '…Sam made her way down to the depot and, after saying 'good morning' to the conductor, she got behind the wheel of the number 73 and began her daily route, moving hundreds of passengers around the city.'
2	**Wednesday**	Inferred from the line: '…there were another two days of work to go after today until she had some free time on Saturday.'
3	**a painting/picture**	Inferred from the line: 'She had decided to remedy this by visiting a local gallery to find something to liven the place up.'
4	**Her job is to drive/ she spends all week driving.**	Inferred from the line: 'It was hard work, and there were another two days of work to go after today until she had some free time…'
5	**other countries/ land**	Inferred from the line: '…her country had no coast…'
6	**a fear of the tiny mountain roads**	Inferred from the line: '…she was terrified of the tiny roads winding up the mountain's side.'

Fiction - Exercise 30 - Family Matters, page 31

Question	Answer	Explanation
1	**two**	Inferred from the line: 'He had older twin brothers and a younger sister…'
2	**winter**	Inferred from the line: '…a younger sister, who had been born the year before, just after Christmas.'
3	**by email/the internet**	Inferred from the line: '…his phone wasn't working, so he walked into the town centre to find an internet café.'
4	**His family were celebrating his mother's new job.**	Inferred from the line: 'All his family were gathering to celebrate his mother's new job.'
5	**given birth to Ryan's sister**	Inferred from the line: '…a younger sister, who had been born the year before, just after Christmas.'
6	**a dentist**	Inferred from the line: '…she was pleased to be getting back to the business of fixing people's teeth, at which she was extremely skilled.'

Fiction - Exercise 31 - Sibling Meet-Up, page 32

Question	Answer	Explanation
1	washing dishes/the washing up	Inferred from the line: 'When Mark's sister, Josie, arrived at the front door, he was wearing plastic gloves covered in soap suds.'
2	He does more housework.	Inferred from the line: '…he did not do much housework of any kind. Things had changed a bit since he had moved into a new residence…'
3	500	Inferred from the line: 'Josie sat immersed in a huge 1,000-page novel of which she had already read half…'
4	She loves it (or similar).	Inferred from the line: '…by which she was thoroughly gripped.'
5	fine/not raining	Inferred from the line: '…the two siblings sat happily in the garden. … It had been pouring with rain that morning so they were lucky…'
6	swimming	Inferred from the line: 'This had not stopped Mark doing lengths in the nearby open-air pool…'

Fiction - Exercise 32 - The Competitive Friend, page 33

Question	Answer	Explanation
1	red	Inferred from the line: 'Philippa leapt out of her red MINI… She was wearing… shorts the same colour as her car.'
2	lights	Inferred from the line: 'He had arrived twenty minutes earlier on a rickety and poorly equipped bicycle, which was impossible to see at night.'
3	disappointed/ cross/annoyed/ unhappy	Inferred from the line: '…he made a face which perfectly expressed his disappointment at his friend's lateness.'
4	normal/fine/good	Inferred from the line: 'Philippa apologised, and said that there had been terrible traffic, which was not true.'
5	Philippa	Inferred from the line: '…vowing to himself that this time he would win their game of tennis. Predictably, this did not happen…'
6	Philippa	Inferred from the line: '…vowing to himself that this time he would win their game of tennis. Predictably, this did not happen…'

Fiction - Exercise 33 - Good Friends, page 34

Question	Answer	Explanation
1	music	Inferred from the line: '…they could enjoy concerts… Simon…had space for a piano.'
2	Priyanka's	Inferred from the line: 'Konrad's place was particularly minute… Simon had a larger place…'
3	Simon	Inferred from the line: 'Simon's friends, Priyanka and Konrad, lived near the centre of town… Simon had a larger place further from the centre…'
4	a teacher	Inferred from the line: 'He worked in a school, and his pupils always did well…'
5	at night	Inferred from the line: 'He often enjoyed listening to obscure classical music until the early hours…'
6	Simon is moving overseas.	Inferred from the line: 'Simon announced that he planned to move overseas…'

Fiction - Exercise 34 - Holiday Delays, page 35

Question	Answer	Explanation
1	She doesn't know what to do.	Inferred from the line: '…Helena scratched her head for a while, then, thinking of a solution…'
2	by driving/by car	Inferred from the line: 'Looking at the flat tyre on her car…'
3	pick her up and take her to the ferry	Inferred from the line: '…rang her mother. She was going to need help if she was going to get to the ferry on time.'
4	her father	Inferred from the line: 'Robert was secretly pleased at this unexpected call; he had been worried about his daughter…'
5	his daughter's driving/safety	Inferred from the line: '…he had been worried about his daughter as she had only recently passed her driving test.'
6	by bicycle	Inferred from the line: 'She would have to cycle the three miles to get it.'

Question	Answer	Explanation
1	**happy**	Inferred from the line: 'Matt walked through the classroom door, smiling from ear to ear.'
2	**next to his best friend**	Inferred from the line: 'He sat down in his usual place next to his best friend...'
3	**He does not like the sweet/liquorice.**	Inferred from the line: 'Matt's expression soon turned into a grimace. He hadn't noticed it was liquorice.'
4	**maths**	Inferred from the line: '...the teacher began the class. She explained some complicated sums, followed by some even trickier geometry...'
5	**Monday**	Inferred from the line: '...the test was at the start of next week.'
6	**Accountants are good at maths.**	Inferred from the line: 'Perhaps his father would help him. He was an accountant and would have no problem explaining this tricky subject.'

Non-Fiction - Exercise 1 - National Geographic, page 38

Question	Answer	Explanation
1	to spread geographical knowledge	Inferred from the line: 'The National Geographic Society was founded…to increase the spread of geographical knowledge.'
2	October	Inferred from the line: 'The National Geographic Society was founded in Washington D.C. in January 1888… Nine months after the society's foundation, the first issue of the *National Geographic Magazine* was published.'
3	24	Inferred from the line: 'It is published monthly…'
4	both inside and on the front cover	Inferred from the line: '…its high standard and extensive use of dramatic photography, particularly on its front covers.'
5	2001	Inferred from the line: 'In 1975, a children's version of the magazine was launched…, but it adopted its current name, *National Geographic Kids*, 26 years later.'
6	They have won many Parents' Choice Gold Awards.	Inferred from the line: '…they have consequently won many Parents' Choice Gold Awards.'

Non-Fiction - Exercise 2 - The Zoological Society of London, page 39

Question	Answer	Explanation
1	They have conservation projects around the world.	Inferred from the line: '…mission is to promote and achieve the conservation of animal species and their habitats around the world… conservation projects in more than 50 countries around the world.'
2	yes	Inferred from the line: 'Its original purpose was to create a collection of animals, a library and a museum, but it has now expanded…'
3	Guy rescued them/ let them go.	Inferred from the line: '…a gorilla called Guy, who regularly rescued sparrows when they flew into his enclosure…'
4	He visited Winnie the bear.	Inferred from the line: '…an American black bear called Winnie, who was visited by A.A. Milne and his son, Christopher, and inspired the Winnie the Pooh books.'
5	It aims to conserve habitats.	Inferred from the line: '…whose mission is to promote and achieve the conservation of animal species and their habitats…'
6	to do with animals	Inferred from the line: '…whose mission is to promote and achieve the conservation of animal species…'

Non-Fiction - Exercise 3 - The London Planetarium, page 40

Question	Answer	Explanation
1	to simulate looking up at the night sky	Inferred from the line: '…taking people on tours of the universe as they lay on their backs and looked up at the night sky…'
2	It was funded by the Peter Harrison Foundation.	Inferred from the line: '…the Peter Harrison Planetarium at Greenwich, which opened in 2007. It was funded with a large grant from the Peter Harrison Foundation of £3.25 million.'
3	a donation of money	Inferred from the line: 'It was funded with a large grant from the Peter Harrison Foundation of £3.25 million.'
4	educational/ entertainment purposes	Inferred from the line: 'Most planetaria in the world are used for educational purposes, but some are used for training in celestial navigation.'
5	There are no landmarks.	Inferred from the line: '…particularly helpful if you are at sea and have no landmarks to help you figure out your position.'
6	a sailor/explorer/ fisherman	Inferred from the line: '…the skill of navigating by using the positions of the stars to help you, which particularly helpful if you are at sea…'

Non-Fiction - Exercise 4 - Giant Pandas, page 41

Question	Answer	Explanation
1	birds and rodents	Inferred from the line: 'Though it sometimes eats birds or rodents, its diet is 99% bamboo.'
2	humans	Inferred from the line: '…because of farming, deforestation and other human development, it now lives in the mountains.'
3	Numbers of wild pandas are rising.	Inferred from the line: '…this number is on the rise. This has led the species to be reclassified from endangered to vulnerable.'
4	It is camouflaged (in snowy regions).	Inferred from the line: 'The animal's colouring provides camouflage in its snowy habitat.'
5	They are inactive/ sleep.	Inferred from the line: 'The panda is active at the beginning and end of the day…'
6	It does not provide it with much energy.	Inferred from the line: '…it can consume large quantities of bamboo each day. However, this provides it with limited energy…'

Non-Fiction - Exercise 5 - The Forth Bridge, page 42

Question	Answer	Explanation
1	**1890**	Inferred from the line: 'Construction on the bridge began in 1882 and lasted for eight years.'
2	Quebec/Canada	Inferred from the line: 'It is now the second longest after the Quebec Bridge in Canada.'
3	trains	Inferred from the line: 'The railway track on the Forth Bridge…'
4	the Firth of Forth	Inferred from the line: '…the Forth Bridge is elevated at 150 feet above the Firth of Forth, which is where many Scottish rivers meet the sea…'
5	wrought iron	Inferred from the line: '…the wrought iron of its contemporary, the Eiffel Tower.'
6	A monument was built to workers who had died.	Inferred from the line: 'It was dangerous work and 57 lives were lost, to whose memory a monument was built.'

Non-Fiction - Exercise 6 - Dirigibles, page 43

Question	Answer	Explanation
1	**1783**	Inferred from the line: 'The first hot air balloon flight took place in 1783… Later that year, balloons were launched that carried animals, and finally humans.'
2	It has a higher density/is more dense.	Inferred from the line: '…the air inside the balloon has a lower density than the colder air outside.'
3	They can be steered through the air.	Inferred from the line: 'Unlike airships, hot air balloons are not propelled or steered through the air…'
4	metal	Inferred from the line: 'Fuel tanks made of aluminium, stainless steel or titanium are now used.'
5	three weeks	Inferred from the line: 'It took 19 days, 21 hours and 55 minutes.'
6	the depth of the earth's atmosphere	Inferred from the line: 'Balloons are able to fly at extremely high altitudes, but cannot rise above Earth's atmosphere.'

Non-Fiction - Exercise 7 - An Industrious Insect, page 44

Question	Answer	Explanation
1	**bees and wasps**	Inferred from the line: '…and to the order Hymenoptera, which also contains flying, yellow and black, striped insects that sting when frightened and sometimes produce honey.'
2	**sterile**	Inferred from the line: 'These large colonies consist mostly of sterile, wingless females…'
3	**They are described as 'wingless'.**	Inferred from the line: '…sterile, wingless females, which work as workers…'
4	**warm and/or moist**	Inferred from the line: 'Ants live almost everywhere in the world, except for Antarctica, but they thrive best in the tropics.'
5	**cooking**	Inferred from the line: 'Human cultures make use of ants for various purposes, one of which is cuisine…'
6	**It (feels like) burns.**	Inferred from the line: '…the fire ant, which takes its name from its venom…'

Non-Fiction - Exercise 8 - Wake-Up Juice, page 45

Question	Answer	Explanation
1	**Africa**	Inferred from the line: '…from *Coffea* plants. These plants are native to Madagascar, Mauritius, Kenya and Tanzania…'
2	***C. Arabica* makes up a higher proportion of coffee grown than does *C. canephora*.**	Inferred from the line: '…*C. arabica*, which makes up 75-80% of all coffee grown, and *C. canephora*, which makes up around 20% of all grown.'
3	**It has a stimulating effect on humans.**	Inferred from the line: '…has a stimulating effect on humans because of its caffeine content.'
4	**Black coffee is popular in America.**	Inferred from the line: 'Black coffee is popular in America, hence its nickname 'Americano' in coffee shops around the world, whereas in the UK, the latte, which is Italian for milk, is more popular.'
5	**in the morning**	Inferred from the line: '…coffee is most often drunk with breakfast, or by commuters when they arrive at their place of work.'
6	**for roughly four centuries/400 years**	Inferred from the line: 'Coffeehouses, or cafés as they are known today, have been popular as meeting points in Europe since the early 17th century.'

Non-Fiction - Exercise 9 - The Lady with the Lamp, page 46

Question	Answer	Explanation
1	**1910**	Inferred from the line: 'Florence Nightingale, who lived to the age of ninety... She was born in 1820...'
2	**Florence**	Inferred from the line: 'She was born in 1820 in Italy and was named after the city of her birth.'
3	**There was social pressure/ opposition for her to become a wife and mother.**	Inferred from the line: '...she announced her intention to be a nurse at the age of 24, despite social opposition and pressure for her to become a wife and mother.'
4	**a large reduction in the death rate**	Inferred from the line: 'She reduced the death rate in the hospital in which she worked from 42% to 2%...'
5	**with better nutrition and medical supplies**	Inferred from the line: 'Nightingale believed that the high death rates were caused by insufficient nutrition, stale air and a lack of medical supplies...'
6	**a lamp**	Inferred from the line: 'She acquired her nickname 'The Lady with the Lamp' by doing regular rounds of the wards at night.'

Non-Fiction - Exercise 10 - Armadillos, page 47

Question	Answer	Explanation
1	**yes**	Inferred from the line: 'All but one species of armadillo live in South America.'
2	**Nine-banded armadillos often have identical quadruplets.**	Inferred from the line: 'The nine-banded armadillo is unusual because it regularly has identical quadruplets.'
3	**cold weather**	Inferred from the line: 'The armadillo's worst enemy is cold temperatures because its body has poor fat stores; therefore, cold weather conditions can have a dire effect on armadillo populations.'
4	**12 times larger**	Inferred from the line: '...from as small as six inches to as large as six feet long.'
5	**their noses/snouts**	Inferred from the line: 'They have poor eyesight, using their sense of smell to hunt prey...'
6	**a hedgehog**	Inferred from the line: '...rather like a certain prickly creature found in England.'

Non-Fiction - Exercise 11 - Chameleons, page 48

Question	Answer	Explanation
1	They can change colour/are camouflaged.	Inferred from the line: 'the chameleon is known for its ability to change colour to match its environment.'
2	signalling (to other chameleons)	Inferred from the line: 'It uses this for camouflage, but mainly for signalling to other chameleons.'
3	no	Inferred from the line: '…are often kept as pets.'
4	a (prehensile) tail	Inferred from the line: 'Chameleons have a prehensile tail, meaning it can be used to hold onto objects.'
5	Its eyes can move independently of one another.	Inferred from the line: 'Their eyes can also move independently.'
6	Its name does not reference its amazing qualities.	Inferred from the line: 'Given this suite of extraordinary features, it is perhaps surprising that the name 'chameleon' comes simply from the Greek words for 'on the ground' and 'lion'.'

Non-Fiction - Exercise 12 - The World's Highest City, page 49

Question	Answer	Explanation
1	its status	Inferred from the line: 'It is not the largest city in its country…but it is the capital of Bolivia.'
2	the opposite	Inferred from the line: '…it rains in summer and is dry in the winter.'
3	the richest	Inferred from the line: '…the richest people living in the lower central areas of the city…'
4	It has a rich history/ Incas lived there long ago.	Inferred from the line: 'La Paz has a rich history: it has been home to the Incas and later, the Spanish settlers.'
5	improved	Inferred from the line: 'Recent political stability means the economy has improved…'
6	It has universities and/or museums.	Inferred from the line: '…La Paz is now home to some of the most important universities in Bolivia, and also the most important museums.'

Non-Fiction - Exercise 13 - The Transistor Radio, page 50

Question	Answer	Explanation
1	**1954**	Inferred from the line: 'The transistor radio was invented seven years after the invention of the transistor, which took place in 1947.'
2	**two**	Inferred from the line: '…the most popular electronic communication device in history, with billions manufactured during the 1960s and 1970s.'
3	**They were portable/could be moved around.**	Inferred from the line: '…sparked a change in popular music listening habits, allowing people to listen to music anywhere they went.'
4	**better sound quality**	Inferred from the line: '…transistor radios were superseded by devices with higher audio quality…'
5	**Other devices can play music of a better quality.**	Inferred from the line: '…transistor radios were superseded by devices with higher audio quality, such as portable CD players, cassette players, mp3 players…'
6	**smartphones**	Inferred from the line: '…today, smartphones.'

Non-Fiction - Exercise 14 - Hang Gliding, page 51

Question	Answer	Explanation
1	**the wing**	Inferred from the line: '…covered with sailcloth to form a wing.'
2	**It does not have one.**	Inferred from the line: 'They rely on currents of air rather than a motor for power.'
3	**a kite**	Inferred from the line: '…they started off as large kites…'
4	**three**	Inferred from the line: 'The pilot is able to control the craft by using a triangular frame…'
5	**speed**	Inferred from the line: 'The pilot is able to control the craft by using a triangular frame, which increases the speed of the glider if pulled.'
6	**a parachute**	Inferred from the line: '…a parachute is incorporated into the harness, which can transport the pilot safely to earth if necessary.'

Question	Answer	Explanation
1	**They live very deep in the sea.**	Inferred from the line: 'Their ability to grow to such huge sizes can be accounted for by their habitat, deep in the sea.'
2	**female**	Inferred from the line: 'Recent estimates put their maximum size at 13m for females and 10m for males…'
3	**They are elastic/ stretchy.**	Inferred from the line: 'Since their bodies have elastic properties, their dimensions remain uncertain.'
4	**no**	Inferred from the line: 'They are related to mussels and other molluscs.'
5	**uncertain/one**	Inferred from the line: 'The number of giant squid species is under debate, but recent genetic research suggests that they are all the same species.'
6	**They live very deep in the sea.**	Inferred from the line: 'Giant squids are deep-ocean-dwelling creatures…'

Other Titles in the First Past The Post® Series

English: Mini-Comprehensions

All books in this series contain 50 exercises, each of which comprises a short passage with six accompanying questions. The aim of these books is to focus on specific question types typically found in the standard comprehension section of contemporary multi-discipline 11 plus and Common Entrance exams: inference questions and fact-finding questions. Each book contains 35 fiction passages and 15 non-fiction passages, and all questions are in standard format. Full answers and explanations are included.

Inference

Inference questions are those which require the candidate to read more deeply into the text to infer the answers from the details given. Answers to these questions are not explicitly stated in the passage. For example, a candidate may be asked how a character is feeling or why a character made a certain action.

Fact-Finding

Answers to fact-finding questions are always explicitly stated in the text, so candidates should be able to answer these questions without any inference or judgement. For example, a candidate might be asked what colour an object is or how old a character is.

Other Titles in the First Past The Post® Series

English: Comprehensions

All books in this series contain 10 tests, each comprising a long passage with 15 accompanying questions. These tests are designed to be representative of the standard comprehension section of contemporary multi-discipline 11 plus and Common Entrance exams. Questions test the student's ability to extract factual information or draw inferences from the text, and some test the student's knowledge of vocabulary, grammar or literary techniques. All questions are multiple-choice, and full answers and explanations are included. Each book allows access to our Peer-Compare Online system, which assesses the candidate's performance anonymously on a question-by-question basis

Classic Literature

All 10 passages in these books are taken from classic fiction books, such as those by Charles Dickens and Louisa May Alcott. These passages contain more challenging vocabulary than modern literature.

Contemporary Literature

All 10 passages in these books are written in the style of modern fiction books, using contemporary vocabulary.

Non-Fiction

All 10 passages in these books are modern non-fiction pieces, such as opinion pieces, reviews and journal articles.

Other Titles in the First Past The Post® Series

English: Spelling, Punctuation & Grammar

These books provide focused practice for spelling, punctuation & grammar. These question styles are tailored towards the last section of the Granada Learning (GL) English assessment, and are designed to test knowledge of the English language. Each book contains 15 spelling exercises, 15 punctuation exercises, 15 grammar exercises and three mixed tests. Each mixed test contains all question types and is designed to provide timed practice. Full answers and explanations are included.

Each exercise comprises a short passage or series of sentences, including a range of classic fiction, contemporary fiction and non-fiction pieces. Candidates must find the spelling or punctuation error on each line, or select the correct word from the options provided so that the sentence makes grammatical sense.